Simple Interfacing Projects

Simple Interfacing Projects

Owen Bishop

Editorial advisor: Henry Budgett

GRANADA
London Toronto Sydney New York

Granada Publishing Limited – Technical Books Division
Frogmore, St Albans, Herts AL2 2NF
and
36 Golden Square, London W1R 4AH
515 Madison Avenue, New York, NY 10022, USA
117 York Street, Sydney, NSW 2000, Australia
100 Skyway Avenue, Rexdale, Ontario, Canada M9W 3A6
61 Beach Road, Auckland, New Zealand

British Library Cataloguing in Publication Data

Bishop, O.N.
    Simple interfacing projects.
    1. Computer interfaces   2. Microprocessors
    I. Title
    001.64'04   TK7887.5

ISBN 0 246 12026 6

First published in Great Britain 1983 by Granada Publishing

Printed in Great Britain by Mackays of Chatham, Kent

Granada ®
Granada Publishing ®

Contents

Acknowledgement

Thanks are due to Henry Budgett for permission to base Projects 8 and 12 on two of the author's circuits previously published in *Computing Today*.

Interfacing to micros

This chapter will deal with a few points about interfacing so that there is no need to refer to them in detail when describing the projects. One point to be considered is how the external electronic circuit is to be connected to the micro. Another point is how the microprocessor is to send instructions to the external circuit or to receive information from it. The way these two operations are to be performed depends partly on your preference and partly on the way your micro is designed. It is important to consider these two points carefully *before* you begin to build your first interface project, so that you may be certain that it will be correctly connected to the micro and that the microprocessor will be able to communicate with it.

This chapter also serves to define many of the terms used in the book, so it is worthwhile looking through the chapter, even if you know something about microcomputer circuits already.

Communications

The microprocessor has three kinds of link with external devices:

(1) *The address bus*, consisting of a set of wires or lines (usually 16, and referred to by numbers, from A0 to A15). The voltage on each line may be either 0V (equivalent to logical 0) or 5V (logical 1). The 65536 possible combinations of sixteen '0's and '1's represent the numbers 0 to 65535 on the binary scale. Each of these is taken as an address. Most of these addresses are allocated to internal circuits, such as the memory, the keyboard and the video output to the monitor screen, but we can allocate spare addresses to external devices. Each external device can be allocated one, or possibly more addresses. The address (or

set of addresses) is reserved for use with that device alone. When the microprocessor wants to communicate with a given device, it makes each address line go to 0V or +5V, so putting the address on the address bus. The device has a logic circuit (the address decoder) which recognises when its address is on the bus, so it knows when the micro-processor is trying to communicate with it.

(2) *The data bus*, consisting of a set of wires (usually 8, numbered from D0 to D7), carrying logical '0' or '1' represented by voltage levels as on the address bus. The 256 possible combinations of eight '0's and '1's represent the numbers 0 to 255 on the binary scale. Signals on the data bus represent *information*, which may consist of coded instructions (the codes being the numbers 0 to 255) or *data* in numerical or other forms. The micro-processor uses the data bus to send information to the external device or to receive information from it. When the microprocessor sends information, we say it is *writing* data. When it receives information, we say it is *reading* data.

(3) *Control bus*, which consists of a set of wires (about half a dozen) which carry special signals between the micro-processor and the external circuits in one direction or the other. We will discuss some of these control signals when we come to look at how each is used.

Connections

There are two main ways in which the communications between a microprocessor and an external circuit are arranged (Fig. 0.1). Many micros have built-in input/output ports (I/O, for short). Usually these consist of special I/O integrated circuits. The i.c.s carry two or three ports each and some micros have several such i.c.s. Usually each port has 8 input/output wires, or channels, numbered from 0 to 7. The ports themselves may be referred to as 'Port A', and 'Port B', or they may be numbered instead.

When an I/O device is used, the address bus goes only as far as the device itself. The I/O acts as an intermediary between the microprocessor and the external device. The external device is connected to the I/O by 8 lines which are, in effect, a continua-tion of the data bus. These lines are used when writing to the

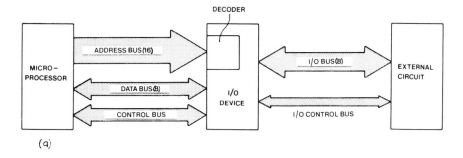

(a)

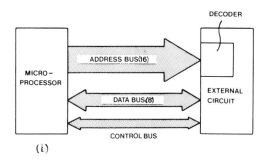

(b)

Fig. 0.1 Methods of connecting an external device to a micro: (a) using an I/O device; (b) direct connection.

external device or reading from it. The main difference between these lines and the data bus proper is that data intended for the external device appears on the data bus for only a short period, while the external device is being addressed. At other times the data bus is in use for communications between the microprocessor and its memory, the keyboard, or other external devices. This means that, unless the device is able to accept the data at exactly the right moment, it will fail to receive it. By contrast, the data being sent from I/O to an external device remains on the lines (it is *latched*) until the microcomputer sends a new item of data to that device. This gives the device much more time to receive that data. The disadvantage is that there is an inevitable delay in setting the output latches of the I/O. This may be of no consequence but, if high speed operation is required, it is better to communicate directly with the external device, as explained below, rather than through the intermediary of an I/O device.

If the system uses an I/O, the microprocessor addresses the I/O, not the device. Then the microprocessor is put into communication with whatever external device happens to be connected to it. The procedure for addressing an I/O depends on the way it is wired into the computer circuits. Usually the handbook that comes with the computer will explain how to use the I/O facilities. Often, the language used on the computer includes special command words. In BASIC, the commands PEEK and POKE can be used to control I/O devices. If your micro already has I/O ports it is probably simpler to make use of these. It will save you the trouble and cost of building an address-decoding circuit for each project. If your micro does not have I/O ports, it is usually better to connect the device in the manner described below.

The second method of connection (Fig. 0.1(b)) is the more direct one. In this, the address bus goes all the way to the external device. This must include an address decoder to recognize when the address of that device is present on the address bus. There are also direct connections to the data and control busses. This arrangement confers the advantage of speed and flexibility, though more care has to be taken over the timing of signals.

One further disadvantage of direct connection, which becomes painfully apparent when one begins construction, is the large number of wired connections to be made between the micro and the external device. With 16 address lines, 8 data lines, the control lines and power lines, we find that a 30-way cable is frequently required. The Z80 microprocessor has an optional mode of operation which requires only the lower 8 address lines (A7 to A0 to be used. This reduces the number of wires needed and also simplifies the design of the address decoder. The BASIC commands OUT and IN are the ones generally used to communicate with the external device. Since only 8 lines are used, the number of external devices is limited to 256. This is more than enough for most people, so a 'port-based' system such as this is often preferred to the 'memory-mapped' system described earlier. If your micro is based on the Z80 or any other microprocessor which can use port-based addressing, you may adopt whichever system you prefer, using an appropriate method of decoding, as described later in this chapter.

Although it is not intended to discuss individual micros in this book, the popularity of the Apple II and the distinctive nature of its I/O features make it worth mentioning. The 8 peripheral slots of the Apple II each have access to the address bus, the data bus and many of the control lines. Most of the circuits described in this book may be assembled on 'cards' which plug in to these slots. The Apple designers have allocated 16 RAM addresses to each slot. These are referred to as the Peripheral Card I/O Space. The addresses are \$COn0 to \$COnF, where n = 8+ slot number. Slots are numbered from 0 to 7. Note the conventional use of the dollar sign which is used to indicate a hexadecimal number. Whenever an address within the I/O space of a given card is being called (by PEEK or POKE, for example), the voltage on the $\overline{\text{DEVICE}}$ $\overline{\text{SELECT}}$ line to that slot drops from +5V to 0V. Thus, most of the decoding is done within the computer, leaving only the lower four address lines (A3 to A0) to be decoded on the peripheral card. In addition to this facility, the Apple II has four annunciator outputs, which can be made to give a high (+5 V) or low (0V) output under program control. Many of the devices described in this book are controllable with fewer than four output lines. If the annunciator outputs are used, interfacing becomes extremely simple and the need for address decoding within the device is avoided. The Apple also has 3 built-in inputs, which accept standard logic levels (0V or +5V). These are also ideal for use with the simple circuits described in this book.

Address decoding

To a certain extent you will need to design your own address-decoding circuit, for the exact connections depend on what address or range of addresses you have allocated to your device. Fortunately, the design of address decoders can be reduced to a few simple rules. These are set out below and, together with the examples shown in the figures will help you to produce reliable decoder circuits.

(1) *How many addresses?* The answer to this is found in the 'Project in Brief' table at the beginning of each project.

(2) *Which address(es)?* This depends on which addresses are already in use in your micro, or have already been allocated to other devices which you have built or have bought ready-made. The handbook of your micro should include a memory map, showing which addresses are used by RAM, ROM, the keyboard, video output, program space, data storage, and so on.

Assuming your micro has 16 lines (or bits) in its address bus, addresses can range from 0 to 65536. This is often referred to as 64K. Unless you have a full 64K of RAM and ROM occupying all the address space there will be plenty of address space which is not being used by the system. Consult the memory map to find out where the free space is. If you have a full 64K system, it is probable that a block of addresses will have been set aside by the designers for I/O purposes as with the Apple II described above.

Whatever the memory scheme in your micro, you should never allocate your device an address in the memory areas reserved for ROM, the keyboard, or the video output. However, you may find that there are small areas within or between these areas which are not used by the system. These are very convenient to use, as they are unlikely to be required for storing programs or data.

If your micro is one of the less expensive kind, you should check how many lines its address bus contains. The micro may use non-standard ways of addressing ROM and RAM in order to simplify the circuitry and reduce the number of lines in the bus. A common effect of this is that certain addresses 'echo' throughout the memory space. For example, see what happens if line A13 is omitted from the decoding.

1001 0000 0000 0000 in binary is $9000 in hexadecimal
1011 0000 0000 0000 in binary is $B000 in hexadecimal

The micro takes these to be *the same address*. It also fails to distinguish between the other pairs, $9001/$B001 to $9FFF/$BFFF. Likewise addresses in the range $8000 to $8FFF are echoed in the range $A000 to $AFFF. If the block $8000 to $9FFF has been allocated to RAM, you can not use the block $A000 to $BFFF for addressing external devices. If you do, the running of a program interferes with the operation of the device in a complicated and frequently disastrous fashion. There is usually a way around this problem but only a close study of the decoding sections of the circuit diagram of your computer will reveal the solution.

(3) *What logic is needed?* To find this out, run through the following routine (Fig. 0.2):

(a) Write out the address in binary form. For example, the address 62220 ($F30C) is written as 1111 0011 0000 1100.

(b) Count the numbers of '1's and the number of '0's in the address.

(c) Every line of the address bus which is to be logical 1 goes to an input of a NAND gate. Every line which is to be at logical 0 goes to an input of a NOR gate. Normally we shall use low-power TTL for decoding. Table 1 shows which is the i.c. to choose.

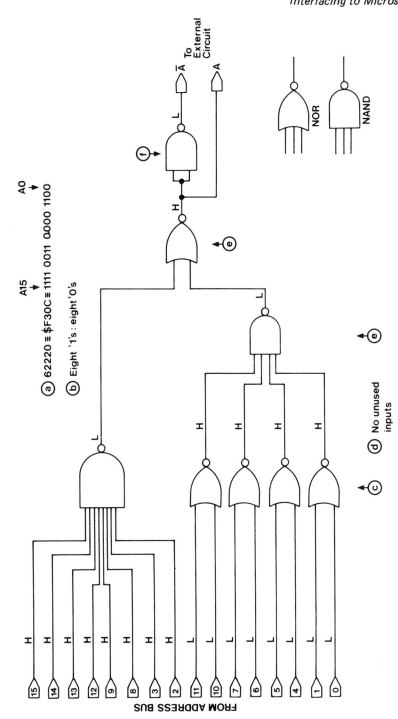

Fig. 0.2 Address decoding circuit for a 16-bit address bus. The circled letters refer to the stages of design listed in the text.

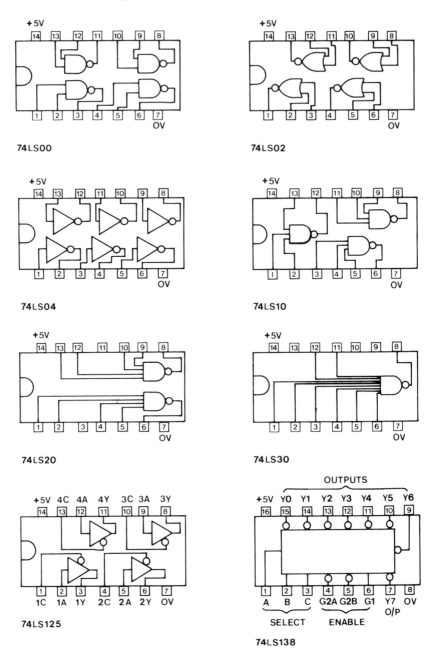

Fig. 0.3 Pin connections of commonly used logic i.c.s, as seen from above. Connections for the standard TTL series (7400 etc.) are identical. 74LS00 = 2-input NAND gates; 74LS02 = 2-input NOR gates; 74LS04 = inverters; 74LS10 = 3-input NAND gates; 74LS20 = 4-input NAND gates; 74LS30 = 8-input NAND gate; 74LS125 = bus buffer gates with three-state outputs; 74LS138 = 3-to-8 line decoder.

Table 1 NAND and NOR logic i.c.s available in low power Schottky TTL (see Fig. 0.3)

No. of inputs	NAND gates	NOR gates	Number of gates in one i.c.
2	74LS00	74LS02	4
3	74LS10	74LS27	3
4	74LS20	na	2
8	74LS30	na	1

na = not available

(d) If there are any unused inputs, wire each of these to one of the used inputs of the same gate.

(e) If more than 1 NAND gate is needed, take their outputs to the input of a NOR gate. If more than 1 NOR gate is needed, take the outputs to the inputs of a NAND gate. Continue in this way until the tree of gates has been narrowed down to a single gate.

(f) If the last gate in the tree is a NAND gate, its output is normally high, but goes low when the device is being addressed ($\overline{A}$, an active low response). Usually, this is the response we need.

If the last gate is a NOR gate its output is normally low, but goes high during addressing (A, active high). If an active-low output is required, the output from the NOR gate is inverted, either by an INVERT gate or by using a spare NAND or NOR gate with all its inputs wired together.

Figure 0.2 shows the stages of designing the decoding tree for the address mentioned above ($F30C). It has eight '1's, so the lines concerned go to the inputs of a 74LS30, which has exactly 8 inputs. The eight lines which carry '0' go to the four gates of a 74LS02. We now have 1 NAND output and 4 NOR outputs to work on. The 4 NOR outputs can be reduced to 1 by using a 4-input NAND gate, in a 74LS20. This leaves just 2 NAND outputs, to be fed to the inputs of a single NOR gate. Note that as you run from any line of the address bus to the base of the tree, the sequence of gates passed through must always be:

NAND – NOR – NAND – NOR – etc. for '1' lines
or NOR – NAND – NOR – NAND – etc. for '0' lines.

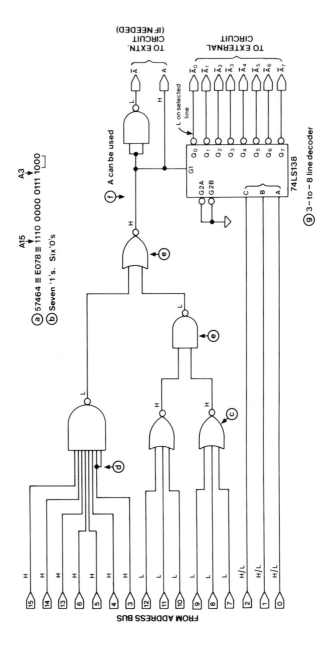

Fig. 0.4 Decoding a block of eight consecutive addresses.

Certain of the projects need more than one address. Different addresses are used for controlling various aspects of the operation of the circuit. Figure 0.4 shows how to design a circuit which will decode a block of 8 consecutive addresses. In the example, the first address of the block (the *base address*) is 57464 ($E078). The procedure is the same as that described before, except that the lower 3 lines are not included. There are seven '1's, but the NAND gate has 8 inputs. This is why line A3 is taken to two inputs. The decoding tree ends with a NOR gate, giving an active-high signal (A) when any address between 57464 (1110 0000 0111 **1000**) and 57471 (1110 0000 0111 **1111**) is on the line. In this block of addresses the levels on lines A3 to A0 may take all the 8 binary values from 000 to 111. It is not worth while to assemble a decoder circuit for the lower 3 lines, since a special 3-to-8 line decoder i.c. (74LS138) is available to do this.

The 74LS138 has 3 'enable' inputs (Fig. 0.4). If G1 is made high, and either one or both of G2A and G2B is made low the chip is enabled. When the chip is disabled, all 8 outputs are high, but when it is enabled *one* of these outputs goes low (active-low). Which one goes low depends on the state of the select inputs at that time. For example, if the address bus carries 57464, the lower three address lines are at '000' and output 0 goes low and outputs 1 to 7 remain high. If the address is 57466, the lower address lines are at '010'; the output 2 goes low and outputs 0, 1 and 3 to 7 remain high.

There is no need to use all the outputs. Unused outputs may be left unconnected. These 'spare addresses' may come in useful at a later stage should you decide to expand the facilities of the circuit. If only the lower 2 address lines are to be decoded, wire 'select C' to 0V.

Should you need to work out how long it takes a decoding circuit to decode an address and change its output accordingly (its propagation delay time), first count the number of gates in the branch of the tree which has the largest number of gates. Allow 10 nanoseconds for each gate. For example, the tree in Fig. 0.2 has a delay of 40 ns. If the tree ends in a 74LS138 decoder, add another 22 ns. For example the circuit of Fig. 0.4 has a total delay of $3 \times 10 + 22 = 52$ ns.

Reading and writing

Microprocessors provide control signals to tell the external devices when an address is on the address bus. Usually there are two such signals:

$\overline{RD}$ used when the MPU wants to *read* data from a device

$\overline{WR}$ used when the MPU wants to send (or *write*) data to a device.

The bar over $\overline{RD}$ and $\overline{WR}$ means that these signals are active-low (p. 12). With the Z80 there is another pair of control lines with similar functions. These are used in the port-based system described on p. 6. The signals are active-low and are called $\overline{IN}$ (low when reading) and $\overline{OUT}$ (low when writing). When $\overline{IN}$ or $\overline{OUT}$ are active only the lower 8 lines of the busy carry an address.

If a device can only provide data or receive data, but not do both, there is no use for any of these signals. We simply use the decoded address signal ($\overline{A}$ or A) to trigger the device into action. If a device can both provide *and* receive data, we need the $\overline{RD}$ and $\overline{WR}$ signals (or the $\overline{IN}$ and $\overline{OUT}$ signals, if preferred and if available) to tell the device which to do. Figure 0.5 shows the logic circuit.

If your micro has a Z80 MPU, decide whether to use the $\overline{RD}$ and $\overline{WR}$ pair or the $\overline{IN}$ and $\overline{OUT}$ pair of control lines. The $\overline{RD}$ and $\overline{WR}$ pair give you a choice of 64K addresses, though most of these may already belong to RAM and ROM, so cannot be used for an external device. Remember too that you must provide 16 connecting wires (and possibly 16 buffers) from the address bus. RAM and ROM are not addressed by $\overline{IN}$ or $\overline{OUT}$ so, by working with this pair of commands you can be certain that you will not interfere with the operation of the micro. You will have only 256 port addresses to choose from, but this is probably more than you will ever need. Using only 8 lines of the address bus means fewer connecting wires, fewer buffers and simpler address-decoding logic.

The 6502 has a rather different system of indicating the read and write states. It has only one control line, called $R/\overline{W}$. This line goes low for writing and high for reading. Again, if your device does only one of these there is no need to worry about using the $R/\overline{W}$ line. Figure 0.5 shows circuits for using $R/\overline{W}$ when your device both provides and receives data.

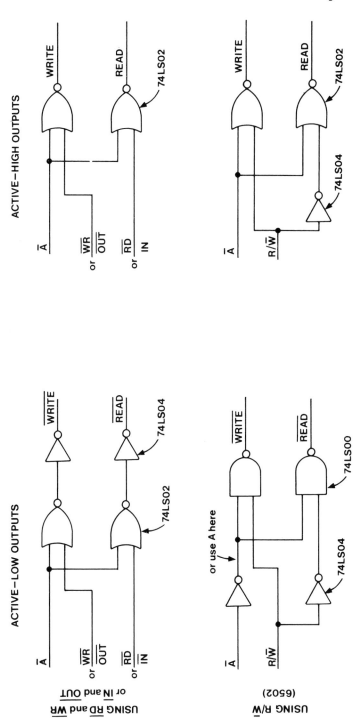

Fig. 0.5 Logic circuits for producing read and write signals.

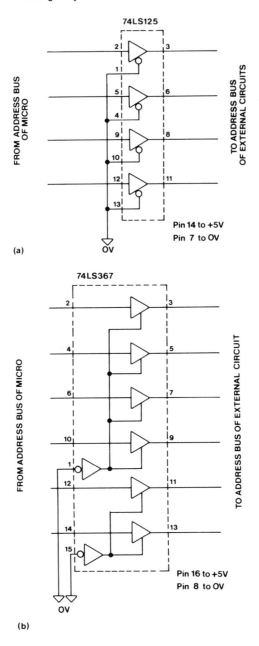

Fig. 0.6 Using buffers between the address bus of the micro and that of external devices: (a) 4 bits; (b) 6 bits.

Connecting to busses

Except in very simple micros, the microprocessor is not usually connected directly to the address bus. Its outputs would not be able to provide the power to drive the inputs of the many other devices on the bus. Each address output of the microprocessor is fed to a special non-inverting gate known as a *buffer*. Figure 0.6 shows the 74LS125 and 74LS367 as examples. The function of a buffer is simply to provide more power for holding the correct voltage level on the line. If your micro uses buffers such as these it can be expected that up to 20 low power inputs (74LS series) may be connected to each line of the bus. If you are merely adding one or two single external circuits on any one occasion, then this adds only 1 or 2 inputs to each line. These are unlikely to overload the computer circuits. However, if you are contemplating adding many such circuits it is advisable to use buffers wired as in Fig. 0.6 to provide the additional power required. The buffers take the signals from the computer bus and transfer them to an external bus. The external bus will drive the address decoders of up to 20 external devices.

Buffers are needed on the data bus too. Here the problem is not to provide power, but to make sure that only one device (be it internal or external) is able to put data on the bus at any one time. The effect of the buffers is to connect or disconnect the device from the bus under the control of the microprocessor. The buffers have what are called *three-state outputs*. The three states are:

$$0V \ (= low = logical \ '0')$$
$$+5V \ (= high = logical \ '1')$$
and high impedance.

The buffers have 'enable' inputs, which are active-low. In the high impedance state ('enable' inputs at +5V) current can neither flow into nor out of the output, so it is for all practical purposes disconnected from the bus and virtually ceases to exist. In the enabled state, ('enable' inputs at 0V, as in Fig. 0.6) the output of each buffer follows the data input ('0' or '1'). All the circuits in this book incorporate data bus buffering. See project 4 for a description of how it works.

Logic levels

Throughout the descriptions above and, indeed, for the rest of the book, we shall quote the voltage levels corresponding to logical '0' and logical '1' as 0V and +5V respectively. Anyone who connects a test-meter to one of the circuits may be disconcerted to find that the voltages in a correctly functioning circuit are not necessarily 0V or +5V. They may lie between these two extremes. A low-power TTL input interprets *any* voltage between 0V and 0.8V as 'low' and therefore equivalent to 0V. It interprets *any* voltage between 2V and 5V as 'high' and equivalent to 5V. Voltages between 0.8V and 2V are not to be tolerated since individual gates may interpret them differently.

Power supplies

Details of power requirements are tabulated in 'The Project in Brief'. Add 5 mA (at +5V) if there is an address decoder. Increase this to 12 mA if the decoder contains a 74LS138. The +5V supply for TTL i.c. must always be a regulated one. If a +5V supply of only a few tens of milliamps is needed, this can often be taken from the +5V line of the micro. Larger loads may be accommodated on micros which have plenty of power to spare. The handbook may guide you on how much the micro will safely supply. It should also tell you what other voltages are available (e.g. −12V, −5V, +12V) and how much current each source can provide.

In some micros the 5V regulator may be fully loaded by existing circuits, but the *un*regulated supply may be able to provide additional current. In this case, you can run a second 5V regulator from the unregulated supply. If no supply can be obtained from the micro, or if you are unwilling to risk overloading its power pack, then you will need to construct an external supply. Circuits and constructional details for power packs are frequently found in electronics magazines and hobby books. Figure 0.7 shows a number of power supply circuits which are suitable for use with the projects in this book. When constructing a power circuit, take special care that bare mains wires and metal parts connected to the mains are not allowed to come into contact with the case (if it is of metal) or with any other part of the circuit. If the case is made of metal, it must be earthed. Wires

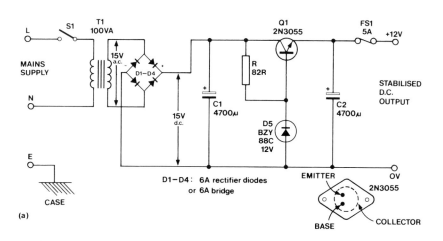

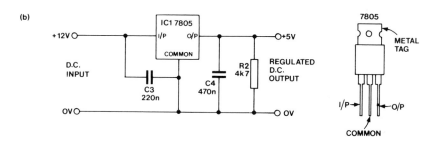

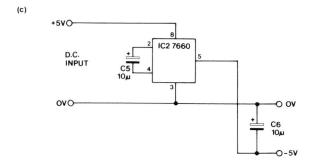

Fig. 0.7 Power supply circuits: (a) +12V stabilized, delivering up to 5A; (b) obtaining a +5V regulated supply suitable for logic circuits, up to 1A; (c) obtaining a −5V supply, up to 40mA.

which are to carry heavy currents should be of sufficiently heavy gauge. The case needs to be of good quality so that it is not likely to burst open if dropped. It should also be well ventilated. The transformer must be securely bolted in position so that it cannot shift if the case is tilted, and will not be torn from its mount if the case is dropped. Power transistors and voltage regulators should be mounted on a heat sink, or have a heat sink bolted to them.

The power supply, the computer and the external devices must all share a common ground line (0 V), so that all voltages are measured relative to this line. In other words, the ribbon cable from the micro must include the micros 0 V line. The 0 V line of the external device and of any external d.c. power supply must be connected to this. In no circumstances should there be any direct connection between the electrical mains lines and the 0 V line (or any other line) from the micro.

Decoupling

Although CMOS i.c.s and low power TTL i.c.s consume very little power, there are times when they require a lot more than their average. A CMOS counter i.c. uses virtually no current when its flip-flops are not changing state, but the demand rises sharply each time one of the flip-flops changes. At the end of a counting cycle, they may all change at once, raising the demand even higher still. Similarly, i.c.s and circuits such as timers and monostables, which rely on the charging and discharging of capacitors, have large requirements at some stages of their operation and low requirements at other stages.

When an i.c. suddenly makes extra demands on the supply it causes a sudden drop in the voltage level of the supply line. At other times the i.c. may generate a sudden increase of voltage (a spike). Fluctuations and spikes on the power supply may easily upset the action of other i.cs sharing the same power supply. Latches and flip-flops are particularly susceptible to being triggered by interference of this kind. One way of avoiding this problem is to provide a reserve of charge by connecting capacitors between the 0 V line and the positive line (Fig. 0.8). A sudden increase in current requirements can be met by the charge stored in the capacitor. A sudden spike on the supply rail is smoothed by the capacitor. Another way of looking at their action is to

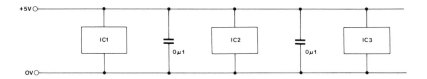

Fig. 0.8 Decoupling the power supply to integrated circuits.

consider the capacitor as a high-pass filter, letting rapid fluctuations of voltage on the positive line pass through to the 0 V line.
In this way the capacitors prevent interference from passing from
one i.c. to the next, so decoupling them.

For normal decoupling, use 0.1 μF polyester or ceramic plate
capacitors. A rough rule is to use one capacitor for every 5 or 6
i.c.s. Since the descriptions in this book do not include detailed
layout of the components, it is not possible to say exactly how
many capacitors will be required and where they should be placed.
Often you will need none at all. For the smaller projects, assemble
the circuit without decoupling capacitors. If it works properly and
reliably, you need not decouple it. If you have trouble with
latches and flips-flops which change state when they are not
supposed to, counters which show erratic counting or inexplicable
resetting, or timers which are continually being retriggered, the
problem can usually be cured by one or more decoupling capacitors. The capacitor should be connected to the power lines
between the points where the malfunctioning i.c. is connected and
the point where a possible source of interference is connected.
Timers (particularly the 555 and 556 timers) are notorious for
generating interference. If this seems to be causing trouble in your
circuit, try wiring a really large capacitor (say 47μF) in parallel
with the power supply terminal of the timer i.c., joining the leads
of the capacitor as close as possible to the power supply terminals
of the i.c.

Constructional methods

The circuits in this book are simple in concept and easy to understand. In common with all computer circuits, a certain amount of complexity may result from the large number of lines in the address and data busses. The small size of the i.c.s with their many closely-spaced pins adds further to the problem of construction. A finely-tipped soldering iron (maximum bit diameter 2.4 mm) and the use of 22 s.w.g. cored solder is almost essential.

Stripboard is very suitable for mounting the components. It is better to use one of the several varieties of stripboard designed for microelectronics. These usually have power-supply busses, tracks laid out ready to accept the i.c.s, an area for the attachment of an edge connector or multiway plug or socket, and may also have an area for taking a 5 V regulator i.c.

If you are adept at laying out detailed p.c.b.s and can cope with running many narrows tracks close together without breaks or overlapping, then the p.c.b. method of construction has features which recommend it. Provided that the original design is correct and carefully checked *before* etching, there will be no subsequent connection errors. This method also avoids the untidy bird's nest of wires which other methods or wiring computer circuits generally seem to produce! Wire-wrapping is another technique which should be considered.

Although most of the i.c.s used in the projects belong to the TTL family and may be handled without special precautions, a few CMOS i.c.s appear in some of the circuits. The details at the beginning of each project tell you if CMOS i.c.s are included. Such i.c.s require special handling:

(1) Antistatic precautions

(a) Assemble the rest of the circuit *first*, add the CMOS i.c.s *last*.

(b) Keep the i.c.s in their packing (metal containers, metal foil or conductive foam) until you are ready to put them in their sockets.

(c) Wear clothing made from natural fibres to reduce danger of electrostatic charges building up on your body. Preferably roll up your sleeves while working.

(d) Cover your working area with an earthed metal sheet (e.g. sheet of kitchen foil); rest your arms on this while handling the i.c.s and soldering the connections. Lay all tools on the sheet when not in use.

(2) Electrical precautions

(a) Do not apply a voltage to any input without switching on the power supply to the i.c. Similarly, do not leave any input with a voltage applied to it when you switch off the power.

(b) When testing partly-built circuits, remember that the i.c. may not behave properly unless *all* its inputs are connected to something. Temporarily connect all unused imputs to 0 V or to the supply voltage.

Project 1
Electric kettle controller

This simple circuit allows you to use your micro to switch an electrical kettle on or off. If the micro has a built-in clock, you can arrange to have the kettle switched on at a pre-set time. Then you can rely on having a hot cup of coffee or tea when you wake every morning. The device incorporates a low-level alarm sounder which you can program to produce a gentle and possibly melodious alarm call.

Table 1.1 The project in brief

Function: A device to control a mains-switching relay and audible alarm.
Interest: Chiefly domestic applications.
Power supplies: +5V d.c. regulated, 10mA; +12V d.c., 150mA; mains supply for kettle.
Address bus: 4 addresses.
Data bus: not required.
Control bus: not required.
Connection: Either direct or through an I/O port.
No. of i.c.s: 1

The circuit controls the kettle by switching a relay on or off. In essence, it is a relay-controller which can be used with any other electrical device which has to be switched on or off. You could make it turn on a bedside lamp or radio set at the same time as it switches on the kettle. A more sophisticated system consists of two circuits like this, one to switch on the kettle and another to switch on the lamp or radio set about 15 minutes later, to awaken you when the kettle has boiled. Other uses for this device include controlling porch lights, room lighting, or low-power electric heaters (but beware of the fire risk should anything combustible have fallen on to, or in front of, the heater). It can switch on lamps under computer control while you are out of the house or away on holiday, so giving the appearance that the house is occupied and deterring potential house-breakers.

Many of the applications of this device rely on the micro knowing what time it is. As will be explained in the section on programming, it is possible to provide relatively rough timing by means of loops in the program. For accurate timing which leaves the micro free to do other things when it is not actively involved in switching things on or off, the micro needs a clock. Projects 2 and 12 tell you how to make clocks suitable for use with the controller.

How it works

The coil of the relay is switched by means of a VMOS power transistor (Q1, Fig. 1.1), which is in turn controlled by the output from a bistable circuit (or flip-flop). The flip-flop is built from two NAND gates, cross-coupled as shown in the diagram. The input lines to the flip-flop are normally high (+5 V or logical '1'). In the 'reset' state, the output from gate 2 is low (0 V or logical '0'). The gate electrode (g) of Q1 is at 0 V too and there is no conduction through the transistor. The coil of the relay is not energised and the switch is off.

When a low pulse is applied to the 'Set' input of the flip-flop, the flip-flop changes state. The output of gate 1 changes from high to low and the output of gate 2 changes from low to high. The high output raises the potential of the gate electrode of Q1, turning Q1 on and so energising the coil. The relay closes, turning on the kettle.

Once set, the flip-flop remains in this state. The relay remains on and the kettle comes to the boil. To turn the kettle off, a low pulse must be applied to the reset input of the flip-flop. This causes the flip-flop to change back to its original state, turning off Q1, the relay and the kettle. It is not easy to make an electronic device which reliably detects when the kettle has boiled. To keep the circuit simple, no provision has been made for automatically turning the kettle off. There are several ways of arranging this. One solution is to use an automatic kettle, which is turned off when a jet of steam blows against a vane connected to a trigger-switch. Another is to use a whistling kettle. In practice, if the kettle is always filled with the same quantity of water and

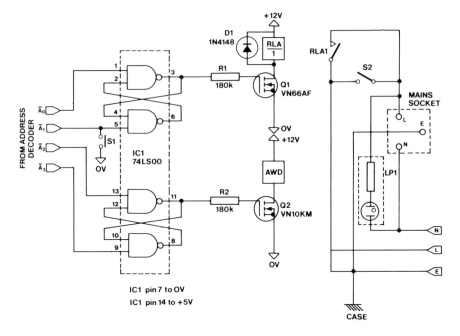

Fig. 1.1 Circuit diagram of the Electric kettle controller.

if room temperature is more-or-less constant, it always takes about the same length of time to boil. All that has to be done is to program the micro to switch on the kettle and then to sound the alarm (say) 10 minutes later. The delay should be almost long enough to allow the kettle to boil. On hearing the alarm you wait a moment longer for the kettle to start boiling and then switch it off manually, by pressing S1.

The kettle has an indicator lamp (LP1) wired in series with it to let you know when it is heating. It also has a manual power switch so that you can use the kettle at times other than those decided by the micro.

The circuit which operates the alarm tone is similar to the relay circuit, except that the relay is replaced by a piezo-electric audible warning device. The diode (D1), which is used to protect the relay-control circuit from high reverse voltages generated when the relay coil is switched off, is not required in the alarm circuit. The type of a.w.d. recommended consists of a thin wafer of piezo-electric material in a case about 1.5 cm in diameter and 3 mm high. To make it sound, the flip-flop is set and reset repeatedly at audio frequency. The way to program this is described later.

The kettle controller requires 4 addresses, a pair for turning the relay on and off, and a pair for controlling the alarm. The address decoding circuit could be like that shown in Fig. 0.4, in which the lower 3 lines are decoded by a 74LS138 i.c. Four of its outputs (A0 to A3) are used and the remaining ones are left unused and unconnected. If the base address is 57464, as in Fig. 0.4, the 4 addresses of the controller are 57464, 57465, 57466 and 57467.

This circuit is *written to* but not *read from*, so there is no need to distinguish between the two kinds of operation. For this reason, the $\overline{WR}$ and $\overline{RD}$ control lines are not used in decoding.

Addressing with an I/O device

The addressing procedure is different if you are connecting the controller to a built-in I/O device (see p. 4) or an I/O device which you have added to your system (see Project 2). The first difference is that the Controller takes the address of the I/O port into which it is plugged. Your micro may already have special commands in its BASIC or other language to allow you to send instructions directly to the port. These may simplify the whole or part of the procedure described below.

The other main difference is that instead of connecting the controller to the address bus and having a decoder to decode 4 addresses, we simply connect it to four lines of one of the I/O ports (Fig. 1.2). These 4 lines (or the whole port if you prefer) are then defined as outputs. This action may be taken care of for you by the command system of the language. Otherwise you will need to consult the handbook of the micro to see how to do this. The way of defining outputs of the 6821 I/O are given on p. 39.

The next step is to set all four outputs to 1 (high), *except* the output which resets the relay-controlling flip-flop. This is made '0', to reset the flip-flop, turning the kettle off should it have been switched on by the relay when power was first applied. Then this output too is made '1'. To set or reset the flip-flops to operate the kettle or sound the alarm, we make the corresponding output low, then high again.

Outputs of the I/O are usually controlled by sending a coded byte to the address of the port. In this code a '1' represents a high output and a '0' represents a low output. To find out what code to send, write a row of 8 binary digits (or bits), with a '1' to represent a high output and a '0' to represent a low output. Remember

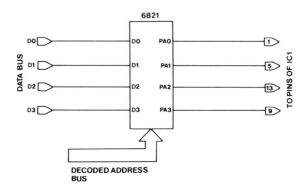

Fig. 1.2 Using a 6821 peripheral interface adaptor i.c. to connect the Controller to a micro.

that the digit on the right corresponds to line 0 and that on the left to line 7. If you are programming in BASIC turn this row of bits into a decimal number. If you are programming in machine code, turn it into hexadecimal instead. For example to make all four lines 0 to 3 go high, the code is:

0000 1111 in binary, or 15 in decimal.

The four '1's on the right represent the four lines 0 to 3. To turn on the kettle, line 0 must be made low but the others must remain high. The code is:

0000 1110 in binary, or 14 in decimal.

This is followed by '0000 1111' to restore the high level to line 0. To turn the kettle off again, the code is:

0000 1101 in binary, or 13 in decimal.

Similarly, codes 0000 0111 and 0000 1011 (7 and 11) control the alarm.

Construction

Wires, bare metal parts and anything else which is at mains voltage must not be allowed to come into contact with the remainder of the circuit. Failure to observe this precaution could lead to serious damage to the user and to the micro. It is safer to build the relay section of the circuit on a separate board. The circuit must be enclosed in a case. This *must* be earthed if it is made of metal.

Choose a case large enough to allow plenty of space between the two boards. This lessens the risk of accidental contact between the mains-voltage and low-voltage sections. When assembly is complete and the lid or panel is screwed in place some of the wires may be forced out of position. Make sure that they cannot accidentally make contact with the mains voltage section of the circuit. Connection between the micro and the controller must not be longer than about 1 metre. If you want to place the kettle in another room, run a long mains cable (15 A) from the controller to the kettle.

Table 1.2 Components required

Resistors

R1, R2   180k   (2 off)

Semiconductors

D1   1N4148
Q1   VN66AF VMOS field effect power transistor
Q2   VN10KM VMOS field effect power transistor

Integrated circuit

ICI   74LS00   quadruple 2-input NAND gates

Miscellaneous

Circuit boards
S1 push-to-make push-button
S2 SPST toggle switch, mains power rated
RLA1 SPST relay, 12V coil, switch contacts rated at mains voltage and able to carry current taken by electric kettle element (suggested rating 20 A).
LP1 Neon indicator lamp with built-in mains resistor
i.c. socket, d.i.l., 14-pin
Mains socket and plug for kettle.
Mains lead and plug for connection to mains supply point.
Edge connector or other multiway plug with ribbon cable for connections to micro (2 ways plus 8 or 16 address lines; 1 additional way of 12V supply taken from micro)
Components for making address decoder (see p. 7)
Components for making +12V supply (see pp. 18 and 19).

The logic circuits can be powered from the micro. It is possible that the micro will also be able to supply enough current to operate the relay. The circuit diagram specifies a 12V supply, but this is only a nominal value. The VN66AF operates at any voltage up to 60 V so, if your relay requires more than 12 V, the design of the circuit is unaffected. The supply to the relay need not be stabilised, so a simple power supply circuit can be built as in Fig. 0.7, using a 12 V 12 VA transformer, a bridge (D1–D4 but use 1 A diodes), a smoothing capacitor (C1) and fuse (FS1, but with a 500 mA fuse), omitting Q1, R1, C2 and D5.

Assuming that the power supplies are available, construction of the main circuit can procede as follows:

Flip-flops

These require 2 NAND gates each, so they are made from the 4 gates of a 74LS00 i.c. For testing, switch on the power. An unconnected TTL input acts as high input so both inputs are effectively high. Measure the voltage at each output. One should be high (more than 2 V, see p. 18), the other should be low (less than 0.8 V).

Temporarily connect a flying lead to the 0 V rail. Briefly touch its other end to the free input terminal of the gate which has the low output. Its output should immediately change to high and stay high, even when the flying lead is removed. The output of the other gate should have changed from high to low. If the flip-flop fails to work as described, check the connections carefully. Look for solder bridges between adjacent tracks and for dry solder joints. Use a lens, for a thread of solder too thin to be easily visible to the eye may be thick enough to conduct a current which can stop the flip-flop from operating properly.

Relay-switching circuit

This comprises R1, Q1, D1 and the relay coil. Since Q1 is to dissipate about 0.6 W when switched on and is to stay on for periods averaging 15 minutes a small heat sink should be bolted to its metal tag. The circuit may be tested by operating the flip-flop as described above and checking that the relay contacts are switched over. A low pulse to the 'set' input of the flip-flop should turn the relay on, while a low pulse to the 'reset' input (or pressing S1) should turn it off.

Alarm circuit

This comprises R2, Q2 and the piezo-electric device. To test it, operate the flip-flop as described above. A sharp click should be heard each time the flip-flop is set or reset.

Mains circuit

The terminals of a relay are often placed very close together. When you solder to the terminals of the switch-contacts, make sure that no bridges of solder or fine strands of wire have contacted the coil terminals. Bolt a mains socket of standard design on the outside of the case. Check that the LIVE lead of the mains supply goes to the LIVE pin of the socket, not to the NEUTRAL pin. When all connections have been made, check again that it is not possible for sections of the circuit which are at at mains voltages to come into contact with sections at lower voltages.

To test the circuit, switch on the +5 V and +12 V supplies. There should be a mains plug on the mains power supply lead, but DO NOT PLUG IT INTO THE MAINS SUPPLY SOCKET yet. Plug the kettle into its socket on the case and connect an ohmmeter across the LIVE and NEUTRAL pins of the mains PLUG. Operate the flip-flop. When it is reset, the relay is open and the meter reads 'infinity' (open circuit). When the flip-flop is set, the relay is closed and the meter shows the resistance of the kettle and indicator lamp in parallel. This is likely to be about 20 ohms (not much less than this). The lamp does not conduct in the absence of mains voltage so its resistance is infinite and does not affect the measured resistance of the kettle when plugged in. Check the resistance between the LIVE pin of the plug and the EARTH pin and also between the NEUTRAL pin and EARTH pin. These should both be infinite. If they are not, look very closely for short-circuits. Switch off the power supplies. Close the case and repeat the resistance tests between the three pins of the mains plug. All three tests should show infinite resistance, for the relay is open.

The controller may now be connected to the micro and plugged into the mains supply. When power is first switched on, the indicator lamp may light or may remain off, depending on which state the flip-flop adopts to begin with. A flip-flop is operated by *any* program command which causes its addresses to be put on to the address bus. You may use PEEK, POKE, IN or OUT or store or load the accumulator (or other register) to or from the Controllers' address using machine code. Any of these actions cause a brief low pulse as the address appears on the bus, so setting or resetting the flip-flop. It is easy to test the kettle control by watching the lamp as you address the BASE address and BASE+1 address alternately. To test the alarm, address BASE+2 and BASE+3 alternately at high speed (see below).

Programming

As explained above, the flip-flops can be triggered by any command which puts one of their addresses on the line. In BASIC, and with a base address of 57464, you can set the controller to switch on the kettle by the command:

POKE 57464, 0

The value which you POKE is a dummy value in this instance. Instead, you could use any command involving PEEK, such as X=PEEK(57464), providing that it is syntactically correct. To turn the kettle off, POKE or PEEK 57465.

Programming the alarm is a little more complex. In the example below you may substitute for POKE a command using PEEK, IN, OUT, STA, LDA or any other equivalent. Once again we take the base address as 57464. The program needs a counter to make the micro repeat the action several hundred times. Here we use a FOR ... NEXT loop. This program sounds a note for about 10 seconds:

```
10 FOR J = 1 TO 1000
20 POKE 57464,0: REM Sets the alarm flip-flop
30 POKE 57465,0: REM Resets the flip-flop
40 NEXT J
50 END
```

This program toggles on and off as fast as is possible with BASIC. The alarm is toggled about 100 times per second, giving a rather low-pitched note of 100 Hz. If you want the notes repeated, delete line 50 and add these lines:

```
50 FOR K = 1 TO 500: REM a short delay
60 NEXT K
70 GOTO 10 : REM to sound another note
```

Unless the BASIC of your micro is very fast or you are using a speedier high-level language, such as FORTH, you need machine code routines for notes of higher pitch. These work so quickly that a delay must be inserted between each toggling. The routine below needs two counters, COUNTER1 to time the delay and COUNTER2 to count the number of oscillations. These are allocated two addresses in RAM which we shall refer to by the names of the counters:

Set COUNTER1 and COUNTER2 to values which give the
required delay and number of oscillations

A: Store contents of accumulator at BASE (sets flip-flop)
B: Decrement COUNTER1
 If COUNTER1 is greater than zero, jump to B
 Store contents of accumulator at BASE+1 (resets flip-flop)
 Set COUNTER1 to its original value
C: Decrement COUNTER1
 If COUNTER1 is greater than zero, jump to C
 Decrement COUNTER2 (counting oscillations)
 If COUNTER2 is greater than zero, jump to A (to produce
 another oscillation)

By varying the value used for setting COUNTER1 we obtain a
different length of delay and thus control the pitch of the note.
By varying the value used for setting COUNTER2 we can control
the length of the note. If the program above is followed by a
second program, identical except for the value placed in
COUNTER1, and if there is a jump back to A following the
second program, the alarm gives out a two-tone note. A note
such as this is much more effective in arousing attention than a
monotone or intermittent note.

This program must also turn on the kettle at a prescribed time
and turn it off again about 15 minutes later. The long delay loops
needed for this are easily implemented. On many micros the loop
below takes about 30 seconds to execute:

```
10 FOR J = 1 TO 30000 : NEXT J
```

You can easily find out how long it takes on your micro. To
obtain a 10 minute delay you merely repeat the loop 20 times:

```
10 POKE 57464,0: REM turn kettle on
20 FOR K = 1 TO 20 : REM 10-minute delay
30 FOR J = 1 TO 30000: NEXT J
40 NEXT K
50 GOSUB 1000: REM Alarm-sounding, as above
60 FOR K = 1 TO 10: REM Wait another 5 minutes
70 FOR J = 1 TO 30000: NEXT J
80 NEXT K
90 POKE 57465,0: REM turn kettle off
100 END
```

The loop technique can also be used for obtaining time delays of several hours. If the main loop gives a 30 second delay it takes 960 such loops (FOR K = 1 TO 960) to give a delay of 8 hours. If the program is started as you go to bed, you will be woken for your morning tea just 8 hours later. It may be feasible to run such a program overnight when the micro is not required for any other purpose, but to run it during the day prevents it from being used for anything else. This is where the Real-time Clock (Project 2) and Alarm Clock Timer (Project 12) become useful adjuncts to the Kettle Controller.

Another project which may be used with the controller is the Mains Remote Control (Project 6). This allows you to have the micro downstairs and kettle beside your bed yet does not require long cables for connecting them.

Project 2
Real-time clock

Adding this project to your micro is like giving it its own watch. The Real-Time Clock is based on a single i.c. which in many ways is like the i.c. you find in an ordinary digital watch. The main difference is that the outputs from the i.c. in a watch are designed for operating a 7-segment ditigal display, but the i.c used in this project has outputs intended to be read by the micro. With the Real-Time Clock installed, the micro can measure time to the nearest tenth of a second and can tell you the time in hours minutes and seconds, the day of the week, and the date (day and month). It also takes account of leap years.

Table 2.1 The project in brief

Function: A real-time clock which connects directly with the micro
Interest: General, accounting, games, educational.
Power supply : +5V d.c. regulated, 110mA.
Address bus: 4 addresses
Data bus: 8 lines
Control bus: System clock ($\emptyset$), R/$\overline{\text{W}}$ or $\overline{\text{RD}}$ and $\overline{\text{WR}}$, $\overline{\text{RESET}}$.
Connection: Through built-in I/O device.
No. of i.c.s: 2 (including I/O device).
Special points: Both are CMOS i.c.s (see p. 22)

How it works

The clock i.c. (IC2, Fig. 2.1) is driven by a crystal oscillator (XTAL1) which is finely adjusted by the variable capacitor CV1. The oscillator is set to 32.768 kHz. A divider in the i.c. divides this frequency by 15/16 to give 30.720kHz. A 9-stage binary divider then divides this by 512 to give 60Hz. This frequency is

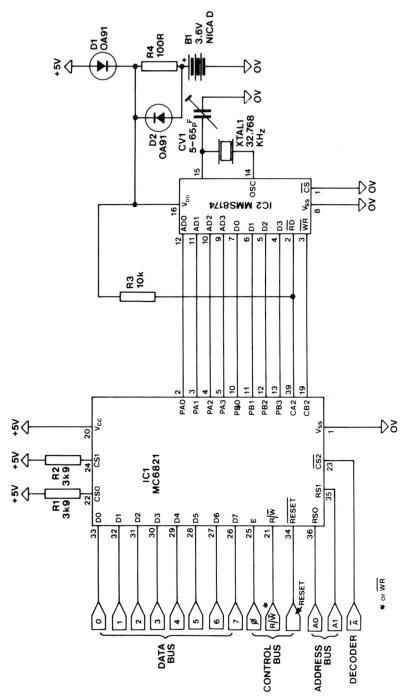

Fig. 2.1 Circuit diagram of the Real-time Clock.

fed to a 3-stage Johnson counter, which cycles at 10 Hz, giving the basic timing cycle lasting a tenth of a second. From then on, a series of counters accumulate the number of seconds, minutes, hours, days, weeks and months which have elapsed since the counter was set. Each of these counts is held in its own register, and can be read by the micro. The micro can also write into each register (except tenths of seconds and seconds), to set the clock with a given starting time, day and date.

The clock i.c. normally operates from the +5 V power supply of the micro. It has a back-up battery (B1) which consists of re-chargeable nickel-cadmium cells. While the micro is switched on, this is trickle-charged through R8 with a current of about 1 mA. When the micro is switched off, the i.c continues to register the time. A minimum of 2.2 V is required to keep it running. Its registers can not be written to, or read from, while it is on low voltage supply.

The clock i.c. is designed for direct connection to a micro but there are problems in implementing this, especially for a design which is to be equally applicable to a wide range of different models of micro. The chief problem is that of timing. To over-come this problem, this project uses an I/O device as an inter-face between the micro and the clock i.c. The I/O chosen is the MC6821, generally referred to as a peripheral interface adaptor (PIA). It is intended for use with the 6800 microprocessor but may be used with other MPUs just as easily. The description below deals with the features of the PIA which are of importance in controlling the clock i.c. It has other useful features which there is not room to mention here, but which are fully described in the manufacturer's data sheet. The 6821 can be used in conjunction with many other of the projects in this book (see 'connections' in the 'Project in Brief' tables), so this project can be taken as an example of how to connect it and how to use it with other devices.

The PIA has 8 data inputs which are connected directly to the data bus of the MPU. Data can pass in either direction along these lines. The other connections between the micro and the PIA are:

∅   the system clock; with the 6800 use the ∅2 line, with the 6205 use the ∅0 line, with the Z80 use the ∅ line; in this application it makes little difference which line is used (should there be more than one).

R/$\overline{W}$ read-write line; with 6800 and 6502 systems the R/$\overline{W}$

line is already provided. If your system has separate $\overline{\text{WR}}$ and $\overline{\text{RD}}$ lines, use an inverter gate from a 74LS04 (see p. 12) to invert the $\overline{\text{WR}}$ line and use this as a $\text{R}/\overline{\text{W}}$ control.

$\overline{\text{RESET}}$ this is the system $\overline{\text{RESET}}$ line

A0, A1 the lower two address lines; these go to two 'register select' inputs of IC1 to select 1 of 4 registers used for controlling the PIA.

You need to decode the upper 14 address lines (p. 9) according to the base address you have decided on for the PIA. The active-low output from the decoder ($\overline{\text{A}}$) goes to the active-low chip select input ($\overline{\text{CS2}}$). If your decoder produces an active-high output you can route this to one of the active-high chip select inputs (CS0 or CS1). The other one of these must be tied to +5 V through a 3.9 kΩ resistor and CS2 must be connected to 0 V.

The PIA has two ports, known as Port A and Port B. Each has 8 lines (PA0–PA7 and PB0–PB7) but the project uses only 4 from each port. Those of Port A are used for addressing the clock i.c. through its address inputs AD0 to AD3. These inputs allow you to select any of the 16 registers in the clock i.c. to set the time or find out what the time and date are. The lines of Port B are used for passing data to the clock registers, or receiving data from them. The clock has its own write ($\overline{\text{WR}}$) and read ($\overline{\text{RD}}$) inputs which are controlled by two control lines from the PIA. The way in which the ports and the control lines are operated is described in the programming section (p. 39).

Reading from the clock prevents the registers from being incremented. It loses time by a fraction of a second every time it is read. This makes little difference in ordinary use, but the clock runs slow if you program the micro to read it many times per second. When the power from the micro is switched off, the output from CA2 to the $\overline{\text{RD}}$ terminal falls close to 0 V. If this were allowed to happen, the clock would stay in the 'read' condition for the whole period during which the power was off and the registers would be 'frozen' at the time when that period began. The solution to this is to wire a pull-up resistor (R3) to hold the $\overline{\text{RD}}$ input at the standby voltage while the micro is switched off.

Construction

The circuit requires very little space and needs only occasional attention to adjust the oscillator, so there is much to be said for mounting the circuit board inside the case of the computer.

It is best to assemble the entire circuit before testing it. In laying out the board, mount XTAL1 and CV1 as close as possible to IC2. Remember that both ICs are of MOS construction so should be handled accordingly (p. 22).

The only useful practical test, before connecting the circuit to the micro, is to apply power to it and use an oscilloscope to confirm that the oscillator is running. When the probe is touched to pin 14 of IC2, an approximately sinusoidal waveform of period 30.5 μs is displayed. Altering CV1 makes little apparent difference to the period, since this is only for fine adjustment of timing.

Before connecting the circuit to the micro, check through all wiring, making certain that everything is correct. If you are using soldered joints, inspect these with a lens, looking particularly for solder bridges and possible dry joints.

Programming

The first topic to consider is the programming of the PIA. The PIA is controlled by means of 6 internal registers, 3 for each port:

Peripheral registers PRA and PRB
These hold data which is being sent to or received from the peripheral (the clock i.c. in this project).

Data direction registers DDRA and DDRB
The data in these registers can be set to determine whether any given line is to act as an input or an output. When a bit is set to '0' the corresponding line becomes an *input*; a '1' makes the line an *output*. Here, as elsewhere in the discussion, 'input' means a flow of data in from the peripheral (the clock i.c.) to the MPU; 'output' means flow out from the MPU to the peripheral. When the system is first reset, all registers are cleared to '0000 0000' so all lines of both ports are inputs. This prevents the PIA from issuing 'unauthorised commands' to the peripheral before the MPU has taken charge of the system.

Control registers CRA and CRB

The bits in this register serve a number of special functions. IRQA1 and IRQA2 (and the corresponding bits in the register for Port B) indicate interrupt status, but are not used in this project. The next 3 bits are used for controlling the CA2 (or CB2) outputs. Table 2.2 shows how these control the $\overline{\text{WR}}$ and $\overline{\text{RD}}$ inputs of IC2.

Table 2.2 Controlling the $\overline{\text{RD}}$ and $\overline{\text{WR}}$ input of IC2

Controlling $\overline{\text{RD}}$ (by CRA)		Controlling $\overline{\text{WR}}$ (by CRB)	
CRA bit values 7 6 5 4 3 2 1 0	Output at CA2	CRB bit values 7 6 5 4 3 2 1 0	Output at CB2
XX111XXX	high	XX111XXX	high
XX110XXX	low (read)	XX110XXX	low (write)

(X = 0 or 1).

Bit 2 of CRA is an important one, for it decides whether the micro is connected to PRA or to DDRA. If bit 2 is set to '1', data addressed to the base address goes into PRA. If, in addition, the lines of Port A are outputs (as in this project) the data appears on the lines and goes to the peripheral. If bit 2 is set to '0', data goes to DDRA instead. This mode is used when we want to set up the input/output status of each line of the port. The same rule applies to Port B.

The lower two bits set of CRA and CRB control lines CA1 and CA2 which are not used in this project.

It requires three different settings of the control registers to operate the clock i.c. The same settings are required for both registers and are summarised in Table 2.3 The right-hand columns give the decimal and hexadecimal values required to effect each command. These values may be used in connection with a statement such as POKE in BASIC, ! in FORTH or store instructions in machine code.

The description above refers to the four addresses of the PIA. The actual base address is determined by the design of the address decoder. The four addresses are selected by lines A0 and A1, which go to the 'Register select' inputs of IC1 (RS0 and RS1) respectively. Table 2.4 is a summary of the addresses.

Let us now see how the clock i.e. is to be programmed. The

Table 2.3 Using the Control Registers of the PIA
(i) *Port A*: Values to be put in CRA (Output CA2 = $\overline{\text{RD}}$)

| Function | Conditions | | CRA bit values | Equal to | |
	CA2	Register	76543210	Decimal	Hex
Ready to put address into PRA	high	PRA	00111100	60	$3C
Read from clock	low	PRA	00110100	52	$34
Ready to alter input/output status of line of Port A	high	DDRA	00111000	56	$38

'Register' indicates which register will be accessed by the base address.

(ii) *Port B*: Values to be put in CRB (Output CB2 = $\overline{\text{WR}}$)

| Function | Conditions | | CRB bit values | Equal to | |
	CB2	Register	76543210	Decimal	Hex
Ready to put data into PRB or read from PRB	high	PRB	00111100	60	$3C
Write to clock	low	PRB	00110100	52	$34
Ready to alter input/output status of line of Port B	high	DDRB	00111000	56	$38

'Register' indicates which register will be accessed by address BASE+2.

sequence for initialising the clock is in Table 2.5. It is essential not to miss out any step. The procedure begins with a reset, as when the micro is first switched on. All registers of the PIA are set to zero and all lines are inputs. The first step is to make four lines outputs on each port. We first address the control register A and input the value 56 to set bit 2 to '0' and make the $\overline{\text{WR}}$ line

Table 2.4 Addresses

Register	Address	Value of bit 2 of control register (CRA or CRB)
PRA	BASE	1
DDRA	BASE	0
CRA	BASE+1	X
PRB	BASE+2	1
DDRB	BASE+2	0
CRB	BASE+3	X

(X = 0 or 1).

Table 2.5 Clock registers

Register number	Function	Read or write
0	Factory test	W
1	Tenths of seconds	R
2	Units of seconds	R
3	Tens of seconds	R
4	Units of minutes	R or W
5	Tens of minutes	R or W
6	Units of hours	R or W
7	Tens of hours	R or W
8	Units of days	R or W
9	Tens of days	R or W
10	Day of week	R or W
11	Units of months	R or W
12	Tens of months	R or W
13	Years (8 = leap year, 4 = leap year + 1, 2 = leap year + 2, 1 = leap year + 3)	W
14	Stop/start (0 = stop, 1 = start)	W
15	Interrupt status (not used)	R or W

high. Bit 2 is now '0' so we have access to DDRA, and the next command puts 15 into this register, causing the lower 4 lines to become outputs. Port B is set in a similar way.

Before the clock can be used its 'test' register (Register 0, see

Table 2.5) must be set to zero. This register is used in factory testing of the i.c. but not by the user. The procedure for setting this register illustrates the general principle of setting registers. PRA and PRB are already accessed so are ready to accept the address of the register ('0') and the data to be placed there (also '0'). Next the $\overline{WR}$ input must be taken low. Provided that bits 4 and 5 are '1', the control output CA2 (which goes to the $\overline{WR}$ input of the clock) always has the same value as is given to bit 3. Sending the value 56 to CRA makes bit 3 low; sending value 60 makes it high again. The effect is a low pulse on $\overline{WR}$, causing '0' to be written into register 0.

Table 2.6 Initializing the clock

To execute the operation, load the register named with the value given. The columns headed 'Outputs' are for use when testing the circuit to see if it is working correctly.

Operation	Step	Register	Value	Outputs			
				Port A 3210	Port B 3210	CA2	CB2
Set lower	(1) Access DDRA	CRA	56	1111	0000	1	1
4 lines	(2) 00001111 in	DDRA	15	0000	0000	1	1
of Port	DDRA						
A as O/P	(3) Access PRA	CRA	60	0000	0000	1	1
Set lower	(1) Access DDRB	CRB	56	0000	0000	1	1
4 lines	(2) 00001111 in	DDRB	15	0000	0000	1	1
of Port	DDRB						
B as O/P	(3) Access PRB	CRB	60	0000	0000	1	1
Put '0'	(1) Addr. 0 at A	PRA	0	0000	0000	1	1
in reg.	(2) Data 0 at B	PRB	0	0000	0000	1	1
0 of	(3) $\overline{WR}$ low	CRB	52	0000	0000	1	0
clock	(4) $\overline{WR}$ high	CRB	60	0000	0000	1	1
Put '0'	(1) Addr. 14 at A	PRA	14	1110	0000	1	1
in reg.	(2) Data 0 at B	PRB	0	1110	0000	1	1
14 of	(3) $\overline{WR}$ low	CRB	52	1110	0000	1	0
clock	(4) $\overline{WR}$ high	CRB	60	1110	0000	1	1

Putting '0' into register 14 *stops* the clock.
Putting '1' into register 14 *starts* the clock.

When you are ready to test the circuit, write a program to put the procedure of Table 2.6 into effect. It will help you familiarise yourself with the operation of the device if you temporarily insert a STOP or BREAK into the program at various points and then use a voltmeter to test the outputs from IC1 at each stage. Table 2.6 shows you what outputs to expect. Outputs of the *unused* lines from Port A are +5 V and the *unused* outputs of Port B are 0 V.

The last four lines of Table 2.6 place '1' or '0' in register 14. This is the on/off register. A '0' stops the clock; a '1' starts it. The usual procedure is to stop the clock, and set the time, day and date. The time is set for a few minutes *ahead* of the correct time. Then, with the program ready to load '1' into address 14, you wait until the set time is reached. Next, let the program run to start the clock at the exact instant.

When setting the clock, follow the same procedure as in the last 4 lines of Table 2.6. Write the appropriate data into each of registers 4 to 13. Note that registers 1 to 3 are for reading only and can not be written into. Register 15 deals with an interrupt facility of the clock which is not used in this project.

Table 2.7 Reading the clock

To execute the operation, load the register named with the value given. The columns headed 'Outputs' are for use when testing the circuit to see if it is working correctly. It is assumed that Port A has already been set as output, and Register 0 has been set to 0, as in Table 2.6.

Operation	Step	Register	Value	Outputs			
				Port A 3210	Port B 3210	CA2	CB2
Set lower	(1) Access DDRB	CRB	56	XXXX	XXXX	1	1
4 lines	(2) 00000000 in	DDRB	0	XXXX	XXXX	1	1
of Port	DDRB						
B as I/P	(3) Access PRB	CRB	60	XXXX	XXXX	1	1
Read reg.	(1) Addr. 3 at A	PRA	3	0011	XXXX	1	1
3 of	(2) RD low	CRA	52	0011	XXXX	0	1
clock	(3) Read PIA	PRB	–	0010	YYYY	0	1
	(4) RD high	CRA	60	0010	YYYY	1	1

X = 0 or 1 depending on values already in registers of PIA.
Y = 0 or 1 depending on value in register 3 of clock.

Table 2.8 Components required

Resistors (carbon, 0.25 W, 5% tolerance)

R1, R2	3k9 (2 off)
R3	10k
R4	100R

Capacitor

CV1	Miniature Trimmer capacitor, 5.5–65 pF

Semiconductors

D1, D2	OA91 or similar germanium diode (2 off)

Integrated circuits

IC1	MC6821 peripheral interface adaptor
IC2	MMS8174 real-time clock

Miscellaneous

Circuit board
XTAL1   32.768 kHz crystal
B1   3.6 V nickel-cadmium battery
40-pin i.c. socket
16-pin i.c. socket
Ribbon cable and edge-connector (14 ways plus 8 or 16 address lines)
Components for address decoder (see p. 7)
Components for +5 V power supply, if micro supply not used (see p. 19)

Table 2.7 shows how to read the clock. Port A is an output, as before, but Port B must be converted to an input. The procedure makes bit 2 of CRB low so that access is gained to DDRB. The value '0' is sent to DDRB to set all lines as inputs. Then bit 2 of CRB is set to '1' again. After placing the address of the register at Port A, the program takes the $\overline{\text{RD}}$ output (CA2) low. This is done by sending the value 52 to CRA. When $\overline{\text{RD}}$ is low the clock puts the contents of the addressed register on its data outputs. These values are fed to PRB in the PIA and can be read by the micro. Use the PEEK command in BASIC, 'fetch' (@) in FORTH or a load operation in machine code. The final step is to make $\overline{\text{RD}}$ high again by writing 60 to CRA. You can read data from any of registers 1 to 12. The information obtained is then used to produce a display or print-out or in many other ways. Sometimes you will obtain the reading '15', which obviously is nonsense. This happens if any register is updated by the clock while you are actually reading it. Updating during a reading could mean errors in a series of readings. Program the micro to repeat the series of readings if any of them are '15'.

Project 3
Bleeper

Whenever this device is triggered by the computer, it sounds a note for a short period. The device can be made to sound for any length of time from a fraction of a second to several minutes. It was first designed as a keyboard bleeper to sound whenever any key was pressed. Many people find it reassuring to have an auditory feedback that the micro has registered the key-stroke and is responding. Other people, who may find it rather irritating to have the computer bleeping away at every key-stroke, can still make good use of this project. If the micro does not have a built-in loudspeaker, the Bleeper can be used to produce sound for use with various games. It can register when a target is hit, or when a player has made a winning move. Since the component which produces the sound may be wired to the end of a long connecting lead, it can be placed in a different room from the micro. If the micro is engaged in a lengthy calculation or other operation, it uses the Bleeper to let you know it has finished, even if you are not in the same room. If the micro has been programmed to warn you when it is time to wake up, to start cooking dinner, or to switch on the TV set, a number of bleepers placed in strategic positions around the house will make sure that you hear the warning immediately, wherever you are at the time.

How it works

The timer i.c. (IC1, Fig. 3.1) is wired so as to produce a single output pulse whenever it is triggered. It needs only a short low-going pulse to trigger it. This is provided by an address decoding circuit with an active-low output ($\overline{A}$). Since only a single output is required from the micro, you should consider the possibility of using a cassette recorder output or some similar output from the

Table 3.1 The project in brief

Function: Produces a 'bleeping' note whenever a key is pressed on the keyboard or when triggered by a command in any program.

Interest: General, games, alarms (including home security).

Power supplies: 5 V d.c. regulated, 10 mA, from the micro but will also work on any unregulated d.c. supply up to +12 V.

Address bus: One address, but may be operated from cassette output or other special output.

Data bus: not required.

Control bus: $\overline{\text{WR}}$ may be required for operation as a Keyboard Bleeper.

Connection: Direct to address bus, or through cassette output or other special-purpose output.

No. of i.c.s: 1

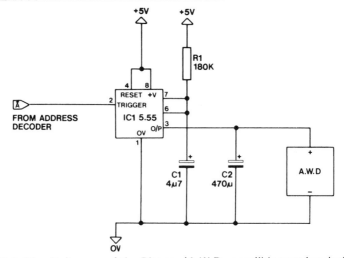

Fig. 3.1 Circuit diagram of the Bleeper (A.W.D. = audible warning device).

micro, so eliminating the need for an address-decoder. Cassette and other outputs vary so much in their characteristics that it is not feasible to provide a design here. Consult your manual for advice on this.

The output of the timer is normally low, but goes high when the i.c. is triggered. The length of time it is high depends on the values of the timing resistor R1 and the timing capacitor C1. The period may be calculated from the equation:

$$t = 1.1RC$$

where   t is the length of the output pulse in seconds

R is the resistance of R1, in ohms

and   C is the capacitance of C1, in farads.

The values in Fig. 3.1 give a pulse of 0.8 s, which is suitable for keyboard bleeping or for most games programs. If you want a longer or shorter pulse, vary the values of R1 or C1. R1 should not be less than 5 K for reliable operation.

The timer i.c. is able to source a current of up to 200 mA (assuming that your micro can supply that amount!), so it may be used to drive the audible warning device (a.w.d.) directly. Several a.w.d.s may be wired in parallel with each other, to give warning sounds throughout the house.

The a.w.d. is one of the inexpensive piezo-electric 'solid-state' buzzers, which have a built-in oscillator. It emits a sound whenever power is applied to it. Most of these operate on a wide range of voltages (typically 3 V to 12 V) and require only a few miliamperes of current. If you want a really loud alarm which could be part of a micro-controlled home security system, for example, you could use a more powerful a.w.d. instead. Such a.w.d.s are generally more expensive but operate perfectly well from a 5 V supply.

Construction

The device and its address decoder, can easily be accommodated on a small circuit board. The sound produced by the a.w.d. is louder if it is mounted on a firm surface, either the circuit enclosure or the circuit board itself. Some a.w.d.s are specially designed for p.c.b. mounting so if you prefer to mount it on the board, obtain one of this type. Other types usually have two lugs by which the a.w.d. may be bolted to any convenient surface. If you are intending to mount the a.w.d. at some distance from the computer, provide two terminal pins on the circuit board and run a twin lead from these to the positive and negative terminals of the a.w.d.

Capacitor C2 acts to smooth the voltage present on the output line of IC1. When the a.w.d. is sounding, it generates a waveform on its positive input line. This may have the effect of re-triggering the timer so that, once triggered, the note sounds indefinitely. You may find that there is no need for C2 with your a.w.d. Try leaving it out of the circuit to begin with. If C2 *is* required, wire it as close as possible to the a.w.d. If the a.w.d. is to be connected on a long lead, C2 should be at the far end of the lead, close to the a.w.d.

Table 3.2 Components required

Resistor

R1   180 k carbon, 0.25 W, 5% tolerance (value depends on timing required)

Capacitors

C1   4.7 μF electrolytic (value depends on timing required)
C2   470 μF electrolytic

Integrated circuit

IC1   555 timer i.c.

Miscellaneous

Circuit board
Audible warning device, piezo-electric type with built-in oscillator, operating on low voltage (e.g. 3 to 12 V)
Components for address decoder, if used
Edge connector or other multiway plug with wire or ribbon cable for connections to micro (3 ways and possibly 8 or 16 address lines)

The Bleeper is tested before connecting it to the micro and the address decoder circuit. Leave the input to pin 2 of IC1 unconnected for testing. Switch on the power. Then briefly touch pin 2 of IC1 with a flying lead connected to the 0 V rail. The a.w.d. should emit its not for about 1 second, the exact time depending on which values you have selected for R1 and C1. Touching a finger against pin 2 is often enough to trigger it.

Programming

The ways in which the Bleeper can be programmed depends partly on the design and firmware of the micro. If it is to be programmed as a Keyboard Bleeper, which is to sound whenever a key is pressed, there are two ways of achieving this. You can connect it to the wiring of the keyboard so that it is triggered by pressing a key. You may know enough about electronics to be able to work out how to do this without interfering with the action of the keyboard. However, this is certain to require additions to the wiring of the keyboard and you should not undertake this unless you are sure what you are doing. There are so many different ways of wiring keyboards that it is impossible to provide any suggestions here for this method of using the Bleeper.

The method recommended here involves investigating the software of the micro manual to find out how the micro deals with key-presses. It may be that there is a certain location in memory into which the MPU places a code corresponding to the last key pressed. Subsequently it reads this memory cell to transfer the code to a 'line buffer' where it is accumulating the codes for the line currently being typed on to the screen. If the manual tells you the address of this location, design the address decoder of the Bleeper so that it has *the same address*. Use the $\overline{WR}$ line to make $\overline{A}$ go low during a *write* operation. In this way the Bleeper is triggered every time the micro writes a new code into this location. This should happen each time a key is pressed.

Instead, you may find that the micro has a particular subroutine in its ROM to which the MPU goes to decode the latest input from the keyboard. If you design the address decoder of the Bleeper to have the same address as the first location in ROM which contains this subroutine, it will sound every time the micro uses this routine. The only point to make sure of is that the routine is not used by the micro at other times or for other purposes.

Once you have found a suitable address which triggers the Bleeper whenever a key is pressed, there is no need for special programming. The Bleeper acts automatically, triggered by the micro's own keyboard routine.

The two addressing methods described above are the only exceptions in this book to the general rule that the address of an interface must NOT be that same as that of any part of ROM or RAM. If you are intending to use the Bleeper for games or to give a warning of some kind, give it an address which is not in ROM or RAM. Do not include the $\overline{WR}$ or $\overline{RD}$ lines, for the address alone is enough. If the Bleeper is to use the cassette output or some other output specially provided for the purpose (as in Apple II, see p. 6), its address can be found from the manual.

The Bleeper can usually be triggered from your program simply by reading from it or writing to it. In BASIC, use the commands POKE or PEEK, together with the address you have selected. In machine code, any operation which would transfer data to it or from it (if it were able to receive or provide data), puts its address on the line and triggers the timer. This simple programming may work when it is connected to the cassette output too, for any disturbance of the voltage level at the output is likely to trigger it.

Project 4
Graphics tablet

If you want to be able to make a drawing, or trace over an existing drawing, and have it transferred to the screen of the micro, this simple device offers one way of doing it. It consists of a base on which is mounted a jointed arm (Fig. 4.1). The arm ends in a pen, a pencil or perhaps a stylus. You fix a sheet of blank paper to the base and then draw on it, using the pen or pencil. As you draw, the line appears on the screen. To trace a drawing or plan you first substitute the stylus for the pen. Then you place the drawing on the base and move the stylus along its lines.

Table 4.1 The project in brief

Function: Drawings made on the tablet are copied on to the screen of the micro.

Interest: Educational, games.

Power supplies: +5 V d.c. regulated, 20 mA.

Address bus: 1 address.

Data bus: 4 lines.

Control bus: not required.

No. of i.c.s: 4.

Connection: either direct or through I/O port.

The Graphics Tablet has two push-buttons. One of these is to indicate to the computer when you are actually drawing ('pen down'), and when you are simply moving the pen from one part of the drawing to another, without making a mark ('pen up'). Press the button for 'pen down'; release it for 'pen up'.

The second button is a spare one which you can use in a number of ways, depending on how you program the micro. It could be used to indicate a change of colour. You might use it to signal 'drawing complete', at which the micro stores the details

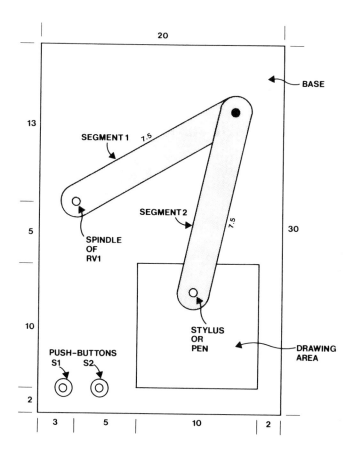

(a)

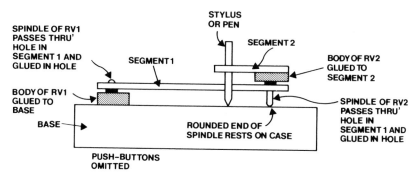

(b)

Fig. 4.1 The main features and essential dimensions (cm) of the Graphics Tablet: (a) plan; (b) front elevation, with the two push-buttons omitted, so as not to obscure the details of mounting segment 1.

of the drawing in memory, clears the screen, and prepares to accept the next drawing.

How it works

The jointed arm is pivoted where it is attached to the base and at the junction of its two segments. These pivots consist of two ordinary potentiometers or volume controls. These are wired as potential dividers (Fig. 4.2) connected to 0 V at one end and to 5 V at the other. The voltage at the wiper depends on the position of the wiper, and can take any value from 0 V to +5 V. In this circuit, only voltages slightly within the range 1.25 V to 3.75 V are used, giving a maximum sweep of about 90 degrees. The body of the first potentiometer (RV1, Fig. 4.3) is fixed to the base and its spindle is fixed to the first segment of the arm. The body of the second potentioemeter (RV2) is fixed to the first segment of the arm and its spindle is fixed to the second segment. If the device is constructed with the dimensions shown, the sweep of each potentiometer is about 60 degrees, keeping its output within the required range.

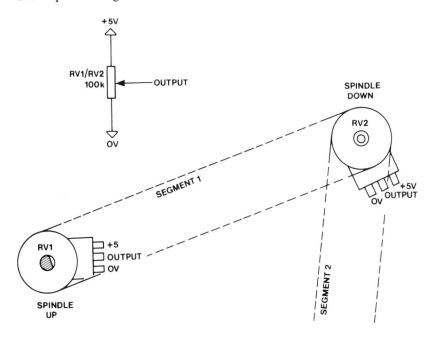

Fig. 4.2 The positioning of RV1 and RV2 with respect to the segments. Inset: electrical diagram of RV1 and RV2.

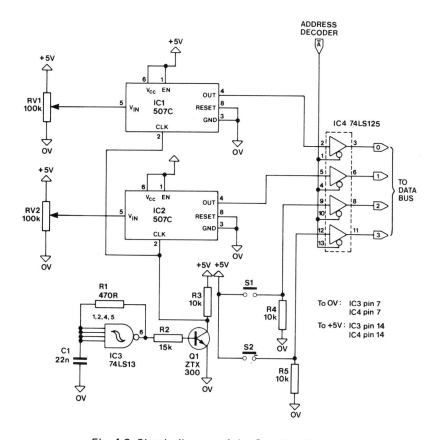

Fig. 4.3 Circuit diagram of the Graphics Tablet.

The joints of the arm can be at any angle within their range. The angle is an analogue quantity. The potentiometers convert each angle into anoher analogue quantity, the voltage at the wiper of each potentiometer.

These voltages are fed to a pair of voltage-to-time converters (IC1, IC2), which work as follows. Each converter receives an input from the clock (IC3) which is oscillating at about 10 kHz. The outputs of a counter which is counting the oscillations are fed to a 'ladder' of resistors in parallel (Fig. 4.4). The currents flowing along these resistors from the counter are summed by the amplifier. The amount of current is weighted by the value of the resistor, so the output from the amplifier is a ramp voltage, falling from 3.82 V to 1.28 V in 256 equal steps. This ramp voltage is compared with the input voltage. If V_{ramp} is greater than V_{in}, the output of the comparator is high (+5 V), but if

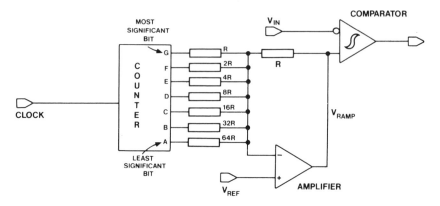

Fig. 4.4 Simplified block diagram of the 507C analogue-to-digital converter i.c.

V_{ramp} is less than V_{in}, the output is low (0 V). The effect of this is to produce a square-wave in which the length of time in the high state is proportional to V_{in}. In this way the i.c. converts voltage to time, yet another analogue quantity.

Though a micro cannot convert an analogue quantity such as voltage to a digital form without some assistance (see Project 8 for an i.c. which does this), it can convert time to its digital equivalent quite easily. It simply has to be programmed to measure the length of the high state of the pulse. The way it does this is explained in the programming section.

The clock used in this circuit is built from a Schmitt trigger NAND gate with all its inputs wired together to make it act as an INVERT gate. It operates by charging and discharging C1, at a rate dependent on the values of C1 and R1. The output of the clock is a square wave but, since IC3 is a low-power TTL i.c., the high level is only a little above 2 V (p. 18). This does not give a swing sufficiently large enough to drive the converters, so Q1 is used to amplify the waveform. It inverts it too, but this makes no difference to the operation of the circuit.

The outputs of the converters go to the data bus of the micro. Data must be put on to the bus only when the micro requests it, so we use buffers with 3-state outputs. IC4 has four such buffers, the two remaining ones being used to convey the outputs from the push-buttons, S1 and S2. When a button is pressed, the output from the buffer is high; when it is released it is low.

Since the computer reads data from this device, but does not write data into it, there is no need to bother about the distinction between reading and writing. The address decoder needs only the address bus, no account being taken of the $\overline{RD}$ or $\overline{WR}$ (or $R/\overline{W}$) control lines. Whenever the computer puts the address of the Graphics Tablet on the bus, the buffers are enabled and the data present at their outputs is passed on to the data bus to be read by the micro.

Construction

The base may consist of a shallow electronics enclosure, the arm and push-buttons being mounted on top and the circuit board inside. The details of the mechanical aspects of construction depend upon the inclinations and skills of the reader. The arm is simple to build, either from plywood or from strip metal or plastic. If you are using wood or plastic, the potentiometers may be fixed to the base or arm segments by means of epoxy or cyanoacrylate adhesive. However, before permanently fixing the potentiometers in position, you should ascertain that the voltages they deliver are within the required range while the pen or stylus is moved round the periphery of the writing area.

The spindle of RV2 is cut to a length which supports the first segment of the arm parallel to the paper. The cut end should be rounded so that it glides smoothly over the surface of the paper.

When constructing the circuit, build and test the clock first. Then complete the rest of the circuit. The output from each converter is monitored by an oscilloscope. As the pen or stylus is moved around the periphery of the writing area, the mark-space ratio (length of time at 5 V divided by length of time at 0 V) of the waveform should vary from high to low, but the output should never be *continuously* low or high. If necessary, adjust the angles at which the potentiometers are set, to avoid both extremes of mark-space ratio as far as possible. Then glue or otherwise fix the potentiometers in position.

The buffers may be tested by making the $\overline{A}$ line temporarily low. The output from each buffer should then be the same as its input. Making the $\overline{A}$ line high puts the buffer outputs in the high-impedance state; a voltmeter then shows a low and indeterminate voltage.

Table 4.2 Components required

Resistors

R1	470R
R2	15k
R3–R5	10k (3 off)
RV1, RV2	100k carbon poteniometer, linear track

Capacitor

C1   22n polyester

Semiconductor

Q1   ZTX300 or similar npn transistor

Integrated circuits

IC1, IC2	507C analogue to digital converter (2 off)
IC3	74LS13 dual 4-input NAND Schmitt trigger
IC4	74LS125 quadruple bus buffer gates with three-state outputs

Miscellaneous

Circuit board
S1, S2, Press-to-make push buttons
Case (see text)
14-pin i.c. sockets (2 off)
8-pin i.c. sockets (2 off)
Materials for making segments of arm (see text)
Edge connector or other multiway plug with ribbon cable for connections to micro (6 ways plus 8 or 16 address lines)
Components for making address decoder (see p. 9)

Programming

The device converts the positions of the segments into lengths of time. The conversion of this analogue quantity into digital form is done by the software of the micro. The easiest way to do this is to program the micro to read the output from a converter over and over again at high speed, to determine how long it is in the high state. In BASIC, the program might be (assuming an address 30000):

```
10 A = 0: B = 0: REM RESETTING THE COUNTERS
20 P = PEEK (30000) : REM IS THE PEN DOWN?
30 IF P < 3 THEN 20
```

```
40 FOR J = 1 TO 100
50 P = PEEK (3000) : IF P = 5 OR  P = 7 THEN A = A + 1 :
   REM READING IC1.
60 IF P > 5 THEN B = B + 1 : REM READING IC2
70 NEXT J
80 etc
```

The program then goes on to plot the position of the pen, as will be described later.

This routine samples the output of each converter 100 times. The longer the outputs are in the high state, the greater the final values of A and B. A and B are in direct proportion to the voltages from the potentiometers and hence the angles through which the potentiometers have been turned.

With a loop which samples 100 times, A and B are known with 1% accuracy. There is little point in trying to obtain better accuracy. There is an appreciable error in positioning already, for the tracks of most potentiometers are not exactly linear (i.e. equal changes of angle at different parts of the track do not produce exactly equal changes in resistance). Such a routine may take about 1.5 seconds to run, which means that the pen must be moved slowly if the program is to keep up with it. It is worth while devising a machine code routine to perform the same operation. This would run possibly 10 times faster, giving conversion in 0.15 s. It samples about 10 pulses from each converter, which is a reasonable number to give good sampling accuracy.

The next stage in programming is to convert A and B to angles, remembering that most micros require angles to be expressed in radians, not degrees. Let us consider RV1 which is at angle 'a' and gives a value A when the program is run. To calibrate RV1, turn segment 1 anticlockwise so that it is in the most extreme position in that direction (Fig. 4.5a). Run the program and call the result A_{min}. You may find that the value of A_{min} is zero, since the i.c. is giving a continually low output. If so, the setting of the spindle in the hole in segment 1 must be readjusted, and you must begin the calibration again. The ideal value of A_{min} is *low* (say 2 or 3%), but not actually zero.

Then turn segment 1 to its maximum extent clockwise (Fig. 4.5b), and measure A_{max}. If you get 100%, readjust RV1 to obtain a value a little less than this (say 95 to 98%) and repeat the calibration for both A_{min} and A_{max}.

If the tablet has been made with exactly the dimensions shown

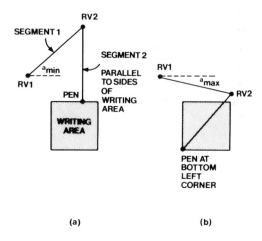

Fig. 4.5 The geometry of the Graphics Tablet at extreme positions of segment 1.

in Fig. 4.1(a), the angles corresponding to A_{min} and A_{max}, measured clockwise and relative to the reference position in which segment 1 is parallel to the top edge of the writing area are:

Value	Angle	Size	
		Degrees	Radians
A_{min}	a_{min}	−42	−0.733
A_{max}	a_{max}	+14.5	+0.253

The total range of angle is 0.986 radians, and this produces a range of values of $(A_{max} - A_{min})$. At any other position of the segment, having taken the reading A, you evaluate the angle a from the equation:

$$a = \frac{0.986 \times (A - A_{min})}{A_{max} - A_{min}} + A_{min}$$

Having established the values of A_{max} and A_{min}, the expression on the right is reduced to a simpler form involving numerical values, except for A. This is written as a single program line to evaluate a.

A similar procedure is used for calibrating RV2. The reference

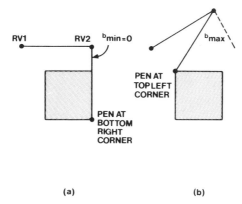

Fig. 4.6 The geometry of the Graphics Tablet at extreme positions of segment 2.

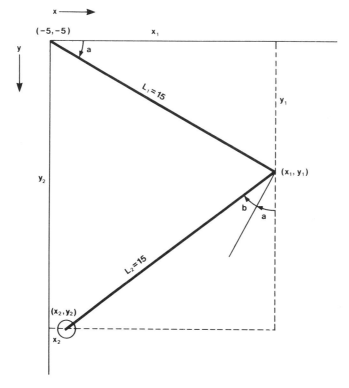

Fig. 4.7 Variables used in calculating the position of the pencil.

position is with the segment 2 at right angles to segment 1. This is also the position for B_{max}. Figure 4.6(a) shows the positions for finding B_{min}. If the tablet has been built to the dimensions of Fig. 4.1, the angle corresponding to B_{min} is 28 degrees or 0.489 radians. The equation for calculating an angle b is:

$$b = \frac{0.489 \times (B - B_{min})}{B_{max} - B_{min}}$$

Figure 4.7 shows how the position of the pen is calculated. The position is measured from the top left corner of the writing area, with the distance along the X-axis being measured from left to right and the distance along the Y-axis being measured downward.

RV1 is located 5 cm above and to the left of the top left corner of the writing area, so its coordinates are (5,5). The co-ordinates of RV2 (X, Y) may be calculated from the equations:

$$X_1 = 15 \times \cos a - 5$$
$$Y_1 = 15 \times \sin a - 5$$

The values −5 and 15 in these equations refer to the location of RV1 and the length of segment 1. The location of the pen is determined by calculating the sides of the lower triangle of Fig. 4.7. The angle we require is the sum of the angle at RV2 (b) and the angle at RV1 (a). X is the difference between X and the base of this triangle:

$$X_2 = 15(\cos a - \sin (a+b)) - 5$$

Y_2 is the sum of Y and the height of this triangle:

$$Y_2 = 15(\sin a + \cos (a+b)) - 5$$

These two equations are written into the program to calculate the coordinates of the pen. These values may then be used to plot the position of the pen on the screen. The way this is done depends very much on the graphics facilities and commands of the machine. If the pen is down, the program will also need to plot points which lie between the present point and the previous point, so as to obtain a continuous line. Many versions of BASIC include commands to do this.

This is a simple and inexpensive circuit which leaves a lot of the work to the computer. The conversions and calculations which the computer is asked to perform make drawing a relatively slow matter, but it is fast enough for many purposes. If you want greater speed, build the Graphics Pad (Project 10). That circuit is much more complex than this one, but it gives the computer the coordinates of the pen with no need for further calculations.

Project 5
Music generator

Nowadays, even the simplest of micros have a built-in loudspeaker and perhaps a routine to 'beep' the speaker. They can be programmed to produce musical notes by toggling the speaker on and off at audio frequency. Notes of different pitch are produced by toggling the speaker at different rates. Producing notes by this method leaves the computer to do all the work. To sound middle C, for example, it has to toggle the speaker on and off 256 times a second. This means 512 operations per second, leaving the micro little time in which to do anything else.

Table 5.1 The project in brief

Function: A 3-channel oscillator producing different musical notes under computer control.
Interest: Musicians, games programmers, experimenters in artificial intelligence.
Power supplies: +5 V d.c. regulated, 10 mA; +12 V to +20 V d.c., 0.5 A to 1 A (for power amplifier, separate power pack advised).
Address bus: 4 addressses
Data bus: 8 bits
Control bus: no lines required
Connection: Either direct or through an I/O port.
No of i.c.s: 5 i.c.s for 1 channel, 6 i.c.s for 2 channels, 8 i.c. for 3 channels. Additional INVERT gate required (from address decoder).
Special points: IC2 and IC3 are CMOS (see p. 22).

The music generator works on a different principle, leaving the computer free to do other things while the music is being played. For example, the music may be part of the sound effects of a game. Using this circuit to make the music, the micro can control the production of sounds while continuing to keep score, to find out which keys are being pressed by the players, and to update the display on the monitor screen. Another important feature is that this project can produce a chord (or dischord!) of up to three notes at the same time, which is impossible with a simple toggled speaker.

Instead of relying on the micro to produce the audio frequencies for itself, the Music Generator has three voltage-controlled oscillators (VCOs, see Fig. 5.1). Each of these produces an audio-frequency oscillation. The frequency of each oscillator depends on the voltage applied to its input. The higher the voltage the higher the frequency. The output from each oscillator is fed to a mixer network. Inputs to the mixer can be set to allow one oscillator to be heard louder than the others. The combined signal then goes to a 2 W power amplifier, which allows you to enjoy an output of adequate and adjustable volume from a speaker of reasonable quality.

How it works

The project was designed to include three VCOs, but there is no need to include all of these to begin with. You can build it with just one or two VCOs or increase the number to four or even more.

To make the VCOs produce different notes, the micro must be able to feed a variable voltage to each VCO. Figure 5.1 shows that each VCO is connected by a switch to a digital-to-analogue converter. The function of the converter is to receive a digital input from the data bus of the computer and convert this to an output voltage. The converter has an 8-bit input, which allows for 256 different values ranging from 0 (0000 0000 in binary digits) to 255 (1111 1111 in binary digits). The output from the converter is a voltage ranging from 0 V to 2.5 V. When this is fed to a VCO, the frequency of the resulting waveform ranges between its lowest and highest limits. The limits of each VCO can be preset.

The switches are CMOS analogue switches, each with its own memory-mapped or port-based address. When turned on, the switch has a resistance of approximately 300 ohms, and current can flow in either direction, charging or discharging a storage capacitor and so raising or lowering the potential at the input of the VCO, until it is the same as that at the output of the converter. When the switch is turned off again the resistance between converter and VCO is about 10^{12} ohms. The potential at the input

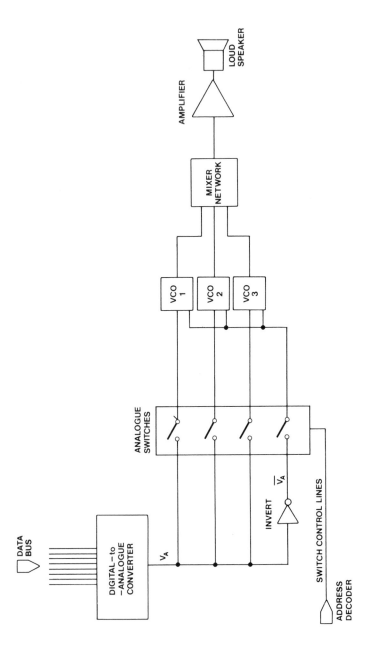

Fig. 5.1 Block diagram of the Music Generator.

of the VCO is held steady by the capacitor and a note of constant frequency is emitted. It takes several minutes for the pitch to fall appreciably. Addressing is decoded so that, when any one of the switches is activated, the converter is enabled at the same time. Its output voltage changes almost instantly and this new voltage is fed to whichever of the VCOs has been switched to it.

The converter works as follows. When the converter is enabled, the data on the bus is placed on a set of eight latches (Fig. 5.2). The outputs of these latches control a set of eight switches. The switches connect the 'rungs' of an R–2R resistor ladder either to the 9 V line, or to a line which is held at a fixed reference voltage.

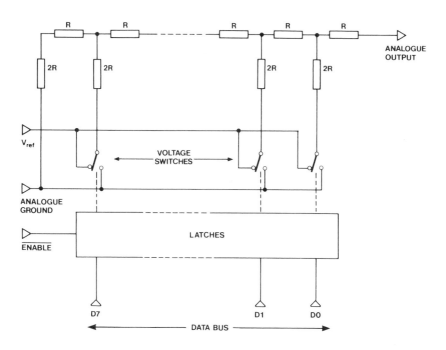

Fig. 5.2 Block diagram of the digital-to-analogue converter i.c., showing details of the R–2R ladder and analogue voltage switches.

The R–2R ladder is an ingenious arranged network of resistors in which the 'rung' resistors have precisely twice the resistance of the others. The exact value of R does not matter, for the network uses the principle of the potential divider. Although it is not so easy to make a chip which carries resistors of a precise value it is easy to ensure that the ratio between different resistors on the same chip is exact. The ladder therefore gives a very precise conversion, yet is cheap to make. The way it works is not hard to understand but rather involved to explain, so it is left to the reader to apply the principles of potential dividers and resistor networks to Fig. 5.2. The voltage delivered by the ladder is:

$$V_{out} = \frac{D}{256} \times V_{ref}$$

where D is the value present on the data bus. For a data input of 0 to 255, V_{in} takes one of the corresponding values between 0 V and V_{in}. These steps in V_{in} are sufficiently small for us to consider that V_{in} varies continuously between 0 V and V_{in}, and can be regarded as an analogue quantity.

The circuit diagrams (Figs 5.3 and 5.4) show further details. IC1 is the D-to-A converter. R1 and C1 are concerned with stabilizing the internal voltage reference of the i.c. Note that there are two ground connections. Pin 9 goes to the 0 V line of the circuit, which is continuous with the 0 V line of the micro. Pin 8 is the analogue ground and must be wired to a point close to the 0 V terminals of the amplifier i.c.s. The output from IC1 goes to three (possibly fewer or more) CMOS analogue switches in IC2. It also goes by way of an inverter to the fourth switch.

One practical problem is that it takes an appreciable time for the current flowing to or from IC1 to alter the charge on the storage capacitors (C2–C5). The brief period during which the micro is writing to an address (a few tens of a nanosecond) is not long enough to allow the charge to rise or fall and the VCO to change from one note to the next. This is the reason for the two timer i.c.s (ICs 6, and 7). These are wired as monostable multi-vibrators, to produce a high-going output pulse lasting about 80ms every time they are triggered by the 'address preset' pulse. The resulting high pulse from the timer turns on a CMOS switch, long enough to allow the VCO input to attain the new voltage from the converter.

IC3, IC4 and IC5 each contain all the circuitry required to build a phase-locked loop, but we use only the VCO section of this in this project. Each VCO requires an external timing capacitor (C6, C7, C8) and resistor (R3, R4, R5). In order to allow for setting the range of each VCO and for fine tuning a preset variable resistor (RV1, RV2, RV3) is provided in series with each resistor. The values indicated in Fig. 5.4 cover the most useful part of the audio frequency range, from 0 Hz (when V_{in} = 0 V) to about

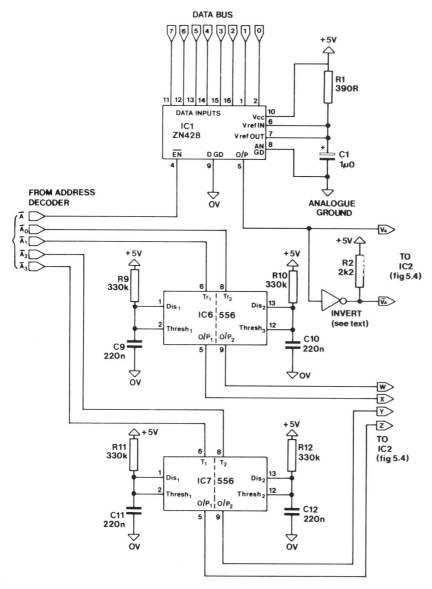

Fig. 5.3 Circuit diagram of the Music Generator: digital-to-analogue converter and switching pulse generators.

2 kHz (when V = 2.5 V, the maximum obtainable from IC1). The resistor and variable resistor wired to pin 12 allow this range to be offset. For example, when their total is about 300 k, all frequencies are raised (offset) by about 64 Hz. The circuit provides for three channels each of which can be made to play different

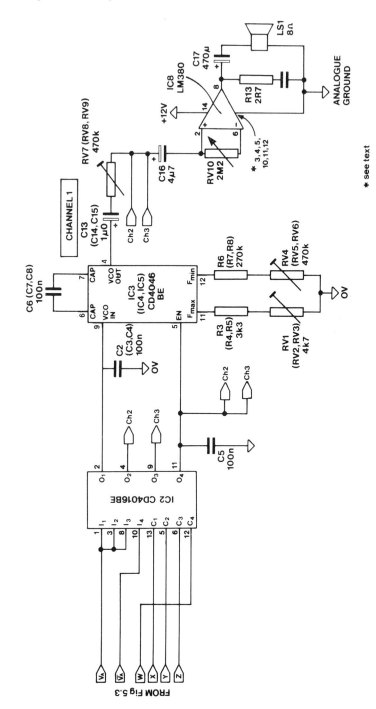

Fig. 5.4 Circuit diagram of the Music Generator: Analogue switching i.s., one of the VCO channels, and the amplifier.

Table 5.2 Connections not shown in Figs 5.3 and 5.4

	To +5 V	To 0 V
IC2	pin 14	pin 7
IC3, 4 5	pins 3, 16	pin 8
IC6, 7	pins 4, 10, 14	pin 7
IC8		*pins 3, 4, 5, 10, 11, and 12 (see p. 00)

All 0 V lines to be joined.

notes. The fourth switch of IC2 is used to turn all VCOs on or off. This allows the micro to produce silent intervals between notes and tunes. The VCOs are enabled when the EN input is made low (O V) and disabled when it is made high. The maximum voltage from IC 1 is only 2.5 V, which is not enough to firmly disable the VCOs. The INVERT gate with its pull-up resistor R2 turns the 0 to 2.5 V output of IC1 into full voltage swing from +5 V to 0 V. The output for each VCO is fed through a capacitor to a mixer network (RV7—RV9).

The variable resistors allow the user to pick out one (or more) channels to be played at full volume for the main melody, while others are heard at lower volume as an accompaniment. The output combined signal then goes to a conventional power amplifier circuit based on IC8.

The address signals are decoded to give an $\overline{A}$ signal based on all but the lower three lines. This allows you to control up to 7 VCOs. A 3-line-to-8-line decoder (Fig. 0.3) provides the signals which trigger IC6 and IC7. When the address of a given channel is on the bus the corresponding output of the decoder goes low. This low pulse triggers the timer i.c. to produce its 80 ms pulse which turns on the CMOS switch. The converter is enabled by the $\overline{A}$ signal directly, without further decoding. The converter is thus enabled whenever any one of the channel is addressed or when the VCOs are to be enabled or disabled.

Construction

It is best to begin by building the output end of the circuit (Fig. 5.4), working gradually toward the micro. If you are intending to build only one or two channels, it is a good idea to use a board

Table 5.3 Components required

Resistors (all carbon, 0.25W, 5% tolerance)

R1	390R	R6–R8	270 k (3 off)
R2	2k2	R9–R12	330 k (4 off)
R3–R5	3k3 (3 off)	R13	2R7

Variable resistors (all carbon horizontal presets, except RV10)

| RV1–RV3 | 4k7 (3 off) | RV4–RV9 | 470k (6 off) |
| RV10 | 2M2 logarithmic | | |

Capacitors

C1	1 μO tantalum bead
C2–C8	100 n polyester (6 off)
C9–C12	220 n polyester (4 off)
C13–C15	1 μ0 tantalum bead or electrolytic (3 off)
C16	10 μF electrolytic
C17	470 μF electrolytic

Integrated circuits

IC1	ZN428E 8-bit digital-to-analogue converter
IC2	CD4016BE CMOS quadruple analogue switch
IC3–IC5	CD4046BE CMOS phase-locked loop (3 off)
IC6–IC7	556 dual timer i.c. (2 off)
IC8	LM380 audio power amplifier

Miscellaneous

Circuit board
LS1 loudspeaker, 8 ohm
Mains on/off switch for power supply (may be built in to RV10)
16-pin i.c. sockets (4 off)
14-pin i.c. sockets (4 off)
Edge connectors or other multiway plugs, with ribbon cable for connections to micro (10 ways, plus 8 or 16 address lines)
Components for making address decoder (see p. 10)
Components for making +12 V supply (see p. 19)

---

rather larger than is needed, so that there is space to spare for additional channels you may wish to add later.

Amplifer circuit

This comprises IC8 and its associated components, including the input capacitors (C13, C14, C15) and variable resistors (RV7, RV8, RV9). Although you may prefer to use strip-board or wire-wrapping for the main circuit, there is a lot to be said for building the amplifier on a separate etched p.c.b. Unless it is operated at minimum power, the amplifer i.c. becomes very hot and heat-sinking is essential. A simple way to provide this is to leave an area of copper (about 15 cm) on the board. Pins 3, 4, 5, 10, 11 and 12 of IC8 are to be soldered to this. The area is con- nected to the analogue ground (the 0 V line of the amplifier's 12 V power supply). If you use a clip-on or stick-on heat sink instead of providing a heat sink area on the board, it is still neces- sary to ground the pins listed above. The return connection from LS1 to C9 must also be taken to analogue ground. If you are etching a separate amplifier board, provide terminal pins for connecting the 0 V rail of the main circuit and pin 8 of IC1 to analogue ground. It is also advisable to provide pads for mounting all three input capacitors and variable resistors, even if you are not intending to build more than one channel to begin with. The input variable resistors are listed as preset resistors, assuming that you will want to vary the relative volume levels of each channel only occasionally. If you want to be able to reset the levels fre- quently, use panel-mounted volume controls (sliding or rotary).

VCO circuits

There are no problems in building these, other than taking the usual precautions when handling the CMOS i.c.s (see p. 22). The values given for the resistors allow the VCO to sweep over a wide audio range. Since the input voltage can take only 256 distinct values, only 256 frequencies can be selected from this range. The wider the range, the less accurately can the VCO be made to produce any desired frequency. You may prefer to sacrifice a wide range in order to be able to tune the VCO more precisely. You may also decide to allot Channel 1 to treble tones, while providing the bass tones on Channel 2. The equations below will help you to calculate the values of resistors and capacitors re- quired:

if   R is the total resistance of R3 and RV1 (ohms),
     r is the total resistance of R6 and RV4 (ohms),
and C is the capacitance of C6 (farads),

then the minimum frequency (when V = 0 V) is given by:

$$f_{min} = \frac{2 \times R}{R \times r \times C}$$

If R6 and RV4 is omitted (making r equal to infinity), the minimum frequency is zero. This is another way of making the VCO silent.

The maximum frequency is obtained when V_{in} reaches its highest value. In this circuit, the highest value of V_{in} is limited to 2.5 V (corresponding to a digital input of 255 decimal). When V_{in} is 2.5 V

$$f_{max} = f_{min} + \frac{1}{R \times C}$$

When you have completed the construction of the VCOs they may be connected to the input capacitors of the amplifier circuit. A potentiometer may be temporarily connected to each VCO in turn, as in Fig. 5.5, to provide an input voltage variable between 0 V and 2.5 V. Switch on the +5 V and +12 V supplies. Turn the potentiometer knob to sweep the voltage between 0 V and 2.5 V and back again. A note should be heard rising in pitch to its maximum and falling to its minimum again. With the values given in Fig. 5.3 the notes at 0 V are an exceedingly low-pitched buzz about (60 Hz). If you prefer not to have such low-pitched notes, reset RV4 to reduce its resistance.

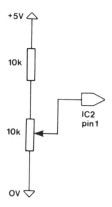

Fig. 5.5 How to obtain a variable input voltage for testing the Music Generator.

Switching circuit

Wire IC2 as shown in Fig. 5.4., connecting outputs O1, O2, and O3 to the VCO inputs (pin 9) of ICs 3, 4 and 5 respectively, to provide individual control of all three channels. Output O4 goes to the enable input (pin 5) of all three VCOs. Solder flying leads to the 4 input pins of IC2. One lead is attached to 11, 12 and 13, the other to 14. Leave the other ends of these leads disconnected for the present. Also solder flying leads to the four control inputs, C1 to C4.

Use the potentiometer (Fig. 5.5) to test this circuit, attaching its output to the input wire which goes to I1/I2/I3. Temporarily connect C4 to the +5 V rail and the four control inputs to the 0 V rail. When you switch on the power, you hear a mixture of these tones. Connect each of C1, C2 and C3 to the +5 V rail in turn. As each is connected you hear one of the VCO channels changing in pitch. Vary the setting of the potentiometer. You can set the tone of each channel by putting the potentiometer to a new position and then taking the corresponding control input to the 0 V rail. Now put I4 to the +5 rail; the sounds stop, for all three VCOs are disabled. Keeping I4 connected to the +5 V rail, connect C4 to the 0V rail; there is no change. Finally, connect I4 to 0 V, and then C4 to +5 V, when the sounds of all three VCOs are heard as before.

Timers

IC6 and IC7 each contain two identical timing circuits (Fig. 5.3). Wire these and their connections to IC2. Make flying leads for the address inputs $\overline{A0}$ to $\overline{A3}$. Note that address input $\overline{A0}$ triggers the timer which sends its output to control input C4 of IC2, whereas $\overline{A1}$, $\overline{A2}$ and $\overline{A3}$ control C1, C2 and C3 respectively. This makes it easier to remember to use $\overline{A1}$ for Channel 1, $\overline{A2}$ for Channel 2 and $\overline{A3}$ for Channel 3. For testing this, apply a voltage to I1/I2/I3, using the potentiometer as before, and connect I4 to 0 V or +5 V as required. Leave the trigger leads unconnected. To trigger a timer to send a high pulse to IC2, briefly touch its flying lead to the 0 V line. Sometimes just touching your finger against the bare end is enough.

Converter circuit

The main point to notice is that pin 8 must be directly connected to analogue ground (the 0 V rail of the power supply) by a separate wire, not simply through the O V rail of the circuit board. The O V rails of circuit board and amplifier board may be joined by some other connection and the O V rail of the circuit board must also be connected to the 0 V line of the micro by one of the leads in the ribbon cable. The output from IC1 goes to pins 1, 3, and 8, as shown. You can probably find a spare gate from one of the ICs used in the address decoder circuit to use as the INVERT gate. You can use a INVERT gate from a 74LS04, a NAND gate (wire all inputs together) or a NOR gate (wire all inputs together). Failing this you will need an extra IC to provide one of the types of gates mentioned.

Address decoder

This should be wired as in Fig. 0.3, except that it may be necessary to use a spare gate to invert A to obtain $\overline{A}$. If your chosen address gives a tree which ends with a NAND gate, this gives the required $\overline{A}$. This may be connected to the G2A and G2B inputs of the decoder i.c. to enable it. Input G1 is to be connected to +5 V in this case. Since this device is written to, but never read from, there is no need to use the $\overline{WR}$ and $\overline{RD}$ lines (or R/$\overline{W}$ line) of the micro.

Testing and tuning

Connect the device to the micro and switch on the power. It is likely that you will hear sounds, probably a mixture of musical tones and buzzes sounding steadily. Controlling the device from the micro is very simple. It has four addresses. The base address is used for switching all VCOs on or off. BASE+1, BASE+2 and BASE+3 are used for controlling the note produced by each VCO. There is no need to control the D-to-A converter itself, for this is automatically enabled whenever any one of the above four addressed is written to.

To test the converter, connect a voltmeter to its output (to measure V_A), with the negative lead of the meter going to the O V line. In BASIC you can use the POKE command (or OUT or something similar). POKE the value 255 to the BASE address. If you prefer to use machine code, load accumulator with $FF and store it to the base address. Whether you use code or a high-level language, the voltmeter needle rises to 2.5 V almost instantly. If is not exactly this value, it is likely that this is because of manufacturing variations in the voltage reference. This makes no difference to the operation of the Music Generator, for you simply compensate for this when 'tuning' the VCOs. If the reading is far from 2.5 V (1.25 V or 1.9 V, for example), it is likely that one of the data lines has a poor connection. If D7 is unconnected for example, the converter receives only '128' when it should be getting '255', so its output is only half what it should be. If you have an oscilloscope you can monitor levels on the data lines where they reach the pins of IC1. You will see a complex waveform which is not at all easy to interpret, but the mere fact that the waveform is there and ranging between 0 V and +5 V confirms that the data is getting through to the converter. At the same time as the needle goes to 2.5 V, sound begins coming from the loudspeaker if it was not sounding already since this command enables the VCOs.

Now send (i.e. POKE, OUT or 'store accumulator') zero to the base address. V_A drops sharply, and sound stops. Sending 128 ($80) gives 0.625 V, and so on. At the same time, you can check the $\overline{V}_A$ output from the inverter. When you send 255, $\overline{V}_A$ is 0 V (sound on), when you send 0 it is 5 V (sound off).

All should now be in working order, so you can try to control the VCOs. POKE 255 to the base address to turn the sound on. Reduce the volume on Channels 2 and 3 to a minimum by adjusting RV8 and RV9. POKE 0 to BASE+1 (Channel 1) to obtain the lowest pitch note. You may want to adjust RV4 to set this to a suitable level. You may also want to adjust RV7 to bring the volume of this Channel up to the loudest you normally want to hear. Try POKEing different values to Channel 1 to see what range of tones you obtain. You may decide to adjust RV1 to increase or decrease the range.

POKE Channel 1 to obtain a tone in the middle of its range then turn up the volume of Channel 2 (RV8) to a suitable level. POKE BASE+2 (Channel 2) with various values and adjust RV4 and RV6 until you have obtained the range you require. Repeat with Channel 3.

To make the Generator play proper musical notes, you will have to discover which numbers are to be POKEd to each channel to produce the pitch required. To establish absolute pitch, you need a set of tuning forks, a well-tuned piano or other musical instrument. If you prefer, you can rely on tuning it by ear. Turn down the volume of Channels 2 and 3. Then find out which POKEd values give the notes you need. A doubling of value should produce a doubling of frequency, and raise pitch by exactly one octave. Make a table of values, for reference. You can make similar tables for the other two channels, but these are likely to have a different set of values for each note. It is generally more convenient to have the same set of values on all three channels. To achieve this, tune each channel by adjusting the presets until the same value gives the same note on each channel. Instead, you may prefer to allocate a different range of notes to each channel. By giving each channel a distinct and smaller range it is possible to tune the notes with greater precision (p. 73).

Here are a few programming suggestions:

(1) Allocate 8 or more keys to each channel (for example, keys 1 to 8 for Channel 1, keys Q to I for Channel 2 and keys A to K for Channel 3). An alternative is to use the same set of keys but 'unshifted', 'shifted' or 'with the Control key pressed' to indicate the channel. The program first POKEs the base address with zero to turn off all sound, then waits for a keystroke. You can use GET$, INKEY$ or possibly INPUT for this. When a key is pressed, the program finds which key it is. The computer POKEs the appropriate channel with the corresponding value for the required note, immediately following this by POKEing BASE address with 255 to turn the VCOs on. It goes into a delay loop to allow the note to sound for a suitable length of time. Then it silences the VCOs and goes back to wait for the next key. This program, alters only one channel at a time. The notes on the other channels remain as they were following the previous key-press. You may prefer to write the program so that a key-press is required for each channel before any sound is produced.

(2) Another approach is to use a set of keys which controls only Channel 1. The program includes a look-up table of chords so that the micro automatically plays chords to every note you play. Maybe it could calculate the chords; for example the note of a major third are in the ratio 1.25:1. The ratio for a minor third is about 1.19:1. Now you are ready to produce an interesting sound as a one-finger player.

(3) The program described above produced notes of fixed duration. You have only to add a small routine to make the program continue to play each note until you press a 'stop key' which for convenience might be the space bar.

(4) Build a set sequence of timings into the program to obtain a definite rhythm.

(5) Let the program store the sequence of key-presses in an array. This holds the tune in memory. A similar program reads from the array and plays back the tune later.

(6) Exploring new territory, you can make the micro select

random numbers and 'play' the result. This in itself may not produce anything more than a boring or even irritating sequence of sounds but, if you give the micro a set of 'rules of composition' to help it, you may get something more interesting. Rules of composition will tell the micro which notes are allowed to follow a note which has just been played. The micro selects random notes so quickly that while one note is sounding it has plenty of time to make many random selections, apply the rules to each in turn and reject each disallowed choice until it hits on one that is allowed. The rules can govern timing, the patterning of ascending and descending passages, repetition of phrases, changes of key, rhythm and many other aspects of composition. It is a good idea to include a storage routine so that when (or if) the computer composes its masterpiece, it is not lost for ever.

Project 6
ROM board

This board carries an Eraseable Programmable Read-Only Memory i.c. (or EPROM, for short). The EPROM has 2 kilobytes of memory which you program permanently, using the special programming circuit provided on the board. Once the EPROM has been loaded with the program, it becomes a convenient memory module for use with your micro. If you wish, you can leave it plugged into the micro, so that the program is always available at power-up. Or you can have a collection of EPROMs each holding a different program, any one of which can be plugged into the 'read' socket (Fig. 6.1) of the board when you want to use it. Programmed with a utility such as a program line editor or a renumberer, the EPROM leaves the whole of your RAM free to hold the program on which you are working. If your games program requires you to set aside a large area of RAM for graphics, the ROM board can hold the games program itself leaving the whole of RAM free for graphics.

The ROM board is presented with a single i.c. but the design may easily be altered to expand it to 4K or 8K. The only change required is the addition of one or more 'read' sockets and a few changes to the address decoder.

Many micros already have sockets into which ROMs may be inserted. If your micro accepts the 2716 EPROM, which is likely, for it is a commonly used type, the ROM Board may be used for programming it.

The program in an EPROM may be erased whenever you have finished with it, and replaced by a new or revised program. It is erased by exposing it to ultra-violet radiation of short wave-length. This is the reason for the quartz window on top of the i.c. You need a special EPROM eraser to do this for yourself, but the hobby magazines often carry advertisements from firms who will erase EPROMs for a very moderate charge.

Table 6.1 The project in brief

Function: Add-on 2 K ROM board incorporating an EPROM programmer.
Interest: General
Power supplies: +5 V d.c. regulated, 160 mA. It is likely that a 5 V regulator circuit will be required (see p. 19), certainly if more than one EPROM is installed. +25 V d.c. unregulated a few mA; can be obtained from mains or from the micro +12 V supply.
Address bus: 2 K addresses
Data bus: 8 lines.
Control bus: $\overline{RD}$ and $\overline{WR}$ (or R/$\overline{W}$).
Connections: direct (own PIA).
No. of i.c.s: 3, plus the EPROM.
Special point: IC1 and IC3 are CMOS.

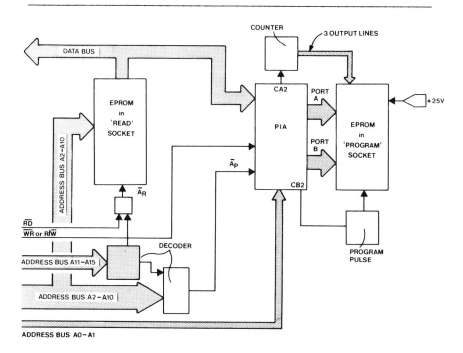

Fig. 6.1 Block diagram of the ROM board.

How it works

There are two types of 2716 EPROM. One of these, the Texas TM2716JL and similar devices, requires three levels of power supply. The type used in this project is the Hitachi HN462716G

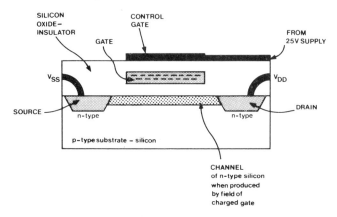

Fig. 6.2 Section through an NMOS gate as used in an EPROM.

and similar devices, which require only a single +5 V power supply when being used as a ROM. When it is being programmed, it requires an additional supply of about +25 V.

The 2716 is an NMOS i.c. and relies on a charge being stored permanently on the gate of the field effect transistor of each memory cell (Fig. 6.2). The +25 V supply is required to provide this initial charge. When first manufactured, the gates are uncharged and all memory cells give a high output (+5 V) when read by the micro. After a gate has been charged the output is low (0 V). Once a gate has been charged, the surrounding silicon dioxide, which is an excellent insulator ensures that it retains its charge almost indefinitely. It does not lose charge when being read from. The field produced by the charge controls holds the FET on or off, but the charge itself is not reduced by the process.

The charge on an EPROM lasts for 10 years or more, so it is permanent for all practical purposes. As mentioned above, the program is erased by intense ultra-violet radiation of short wavelength. This is strongly ionising and discharges the gates in about half an hour.

When being used in the 'read' socket, the i.c. has 11 inputs from the address bus (Figs 6.1 and 6.3). The base address is set by the levels required on the upper 5 lines to enable the address decoder. Figure 6.3 shows one possible decoder. When the lines are 111000, and the $\overline{RD}$ (read line is low), a low level appears on the $\overline{A}_R$ line. This is connected to the output enable ($\overline{OE}$) pin. A low level there causes the EPROM to put the addressed byte of data on to the data bus.

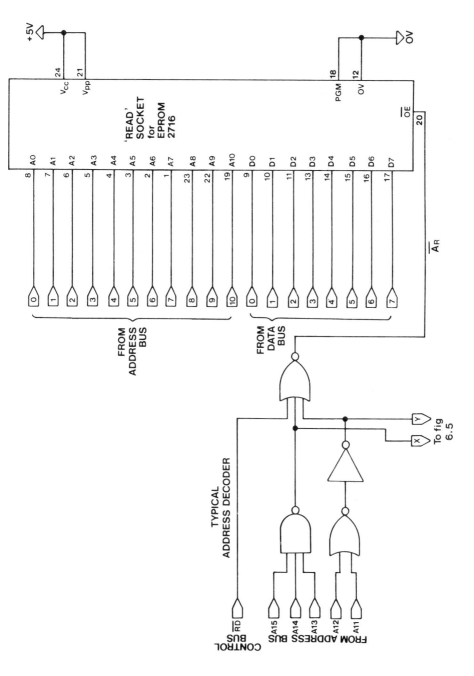

Fig. 6.3 Circuit diagram of the ROM Board: 'Read' socket.

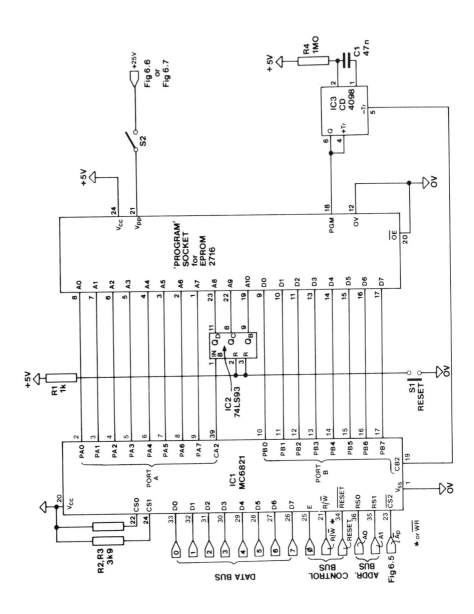

Fig. 6.4 Circuit diagram of the ROM Board: 'Program' socket and PIA.

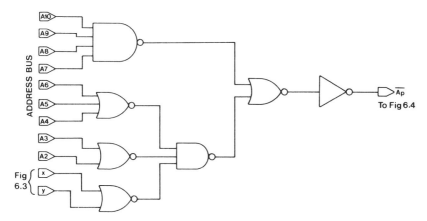

Fig. 6.5 An address decoder for the PIA of Fig. 6.4, using inputs from the decoder of Fig. 6.3.

In the 'read' socket its V_{pp} input is held at +5 V and its PGM (program) input is held low. For programming, the EPROM is placed in the 'program' socket (Fig. 6.4) in which the Vpp input is connected to a +25 V source and PGM is connected to a pulse generator. The address and data inputs to the EPROM come from a 6821 peripheral interface adaptor. The way this PIA works is described on p. 37.

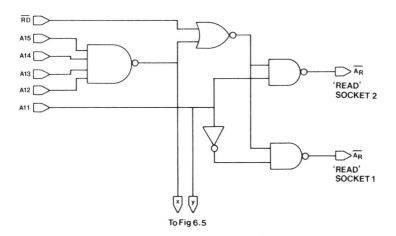

Fig. 6.6 An address decoder for use with two 'Read' sockets.

When a memory cell has been addressed and the data to be put in that cell is on the data inputs the cell is programmed by a

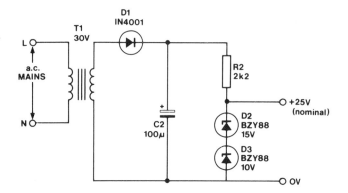

Fig. 6.7 Circuit for the +25 V programming current.

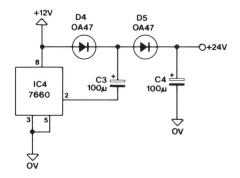

Fig. 6.8 Voltage-doubling circuit for the +25 V programming current.

pulse from the programming pulse generator. The pulse-generator consists of a monostable multivibrator (IC3) which is triggered by a low pulse from CB2.

Two alternative +25 V sources are suggested. The first (Fig. 6.7) uses the mains supply, a transformer and a half-wave rectifier circuit (D1). Two zener diodes (D2, D3) hold the potential of C1 at approximately 25V. The second (Fig. 6.8) uses the 7660 voltage converter i.c. in a voltage-doubling circuit. This requires a +12 V d.c. supply, which the micro may be able to provide.

Construction

It is advisable to use a board that is large enough to allow for expansion, should you subsequently decide to add another EPROM or two. There are no special problems of construction, except that if your system already has a relatively large number of i.c.s attached to the address bus it may be advisable to wire buffers between the bus and the EPROM(s). When laying out the board, try to keep all bus lines as short as possible. The programming socket and the PIA should be as close together as is convenient. Also make sure that there is no way in which the +25 V line or any lines at mains voltage can accidentally come into contact with the low-voltage wiring, particularly that which connects directly to the micro.

IC3 has two multivibrators, of which only one is used in this circuit. Because this is a CMOS i.c. it is essential that the input terminals of the other multivibrator are connected to +5 V or to 0 V, as listed in Table 6.2.

Table 6.2 Connections not shown in Figs 6.3 and 6.4

	To 0 V	To +5 V
IC2	Pin 10	Pins 5, 14
IC3	Pins 8, 12, 13	Pins 3, 11, 16

If you are installing a single read 'socket', use an address decoder similar to that of Fig. 6.3. A typical address decoder for the PIA is shown in Fig. 6.5. If there are to be two or three read 'sockets' (assuming that you can spare a large enough block of memory in your micro) run the address lines and data lines to both or all sockets. Each socket has a separate line from its own address decoder (see Fig. 6.6).

Programming

No special programming is required to read the EPROM once it has been programmed and put in the 'read socket'. It behaves in just the same way as any other section of ROM. The maximum access time of the 2716 is 450 ns, which is the same for most of the commonly available EPROMs.

In programming the EPROM, it is normally loaded with machine code though there is no reason why you should not use it for storing a program in BASIC or any other high-level language. FORTH programs are compact and are very suitable for loading

Table 6.3 Components required

(a) Main board, excluding 25 V supply

Resistors (carbon, 0.25W, 5% tolerance)

R1   1k
R2, R3 3k9
R4   1MO

Capacitors

C1   47n ceramic
        An electrolytic capacitor, 100 μF is recommended between the 0 V
        and +5 V lines if the supply is taken from the micro

Integrated circuits

IC1   MC6821 peripheral interface adapter
IC2   74LS93 4-bit binary counter
IC3   CD4098BE dual monostable multivibrator
        2716 EPROM (1 or more)

Miscellaneous

Circuit board
S1   Push-to-make push-button
S2   SPST toggle switch
40-pin i.c. socket
24-pin i.c. sockets (2 off, more if extra EPROMs fitted)
16-pin i.c. socket
14-pin i.c. socket
Edge-connector or other multiway plug with ribbon cable for connections to
micro (29 ways)
Components for making address decoders (see p. 7, Figs 6.3, 6.5 and 6.6)

(b) Mains-sourced 25 V supply (Fig. 6.7)

Resistor

R2   2k2 carbon, 0.25W, 5% tolerance

Capacitor

C2   100 μF electrolytic

Semiconductors

D1   1N4001 rectifier diode
D2   BZY88, 15 V zener diode
D3   BZY88, 10 V zener diode

Table 6.3 Contd.

Miscellaneous

T1   Mains transformer, 30 V secondary, 3 VA
Mains cable and plug

(c) Micro-sourced 25 V supply (Fig. 6.8)

Capacitors

C3, C4   100 μF, electrolytic

Semiconductors

D4, D5   OA47 or similar germanium diodes

Integrated Circuit

IC4   7660 voltage converter

---

into EPROMs, especially for use with small microprocessor-based control systems. To load a program into the EPROM, the program is first of all loaded into a block of RAM in the micro. Check that the number of bytes does not exceed 2 K. Check also that there are no mistakes in the loaded program, for it is easy to correct these now. If the error is discovered later after the EPROM has been programmed, the i.c. must be completely erased and re-programmed. It is not possible to correct individual bits or bytes. It is a good idea to RUN the program to make sure that it is working properly.

Table 6.4 shows the sequence of operations needed for programming the EPROM. It can be written in machine code or a high-level language such as BASIC. The program needs two software counters, called BYTES and QUARTERS, whose function is described below. In machine code, these will be two addresses in RAM set aside for the purpose; in BASIC, these can be two variables, such as B and Q.

Before running the program, plug the EPROM into the programming socket, but do not switch on the 25 V supply yet (S2 open). Run the first stage of the program which defines the outputs from the PIA. Then press the reset button (S1) so that the output from the hardware counter, IC4, is cleared to all zeros. Now it is safe to switch on the 25 V supply (S2 closed).

Run the remainder of the program, which takes about 100

Table 6.4 Programming the EPROM

To execute the operation, load the register named with the value given. The columns headed 'Outputs' are for use when testing the circuit to see if it is working correctly. BYTES is the value in the BYTES counter (initially 0), and is used as the address in the EPROM (relative to the beginning of the current quarter-kilobyte). QUARTERS is the value in the QUARTERS counter and also the output from IC3, both of which are initially 0 and both of which indicate the starting address in the EPROM of the current quarter kilobyte IF BASE is the first address of the block of RAM in which the data is stored, the address from which the current byte of DATA should be read prior to loading it into the EPROM is found by calculating BASE + BYTES + 256 × QUARTERS.

Operation	Step	Register	Value	Port A	Port B	CA2	CB2
Set all	(1) Access DDRA	CRA	56	all 1	all 0	1	0
Port A	(2) 11111111 in	DDRA	255	all 0	all 0	1	0
as	DDRA						
outputs	(3) Access PRA	CRA	60	all 0	all 0	1	0
Set all	(1) Access DDRB	CRB	56	all 0	all 0	1	1
Port B	(2) 11111111 in	DDRB	255	all 0	all 0	1	1
as	DDRB						
outputs	(3) Access PRB	CRB	60	all 0	all 0	1	1

Press 'Reset' button (S1)
Switch on 25 V supply (S2)

Put DATA	(1) BYTES at A	PRA	BYTES	BYTES	all 0	1	1
in addr.	(2) DATA at B	PRB	DATA	BYTES	DATA	1	1
BYTES &	(3) CB2 low	CRB	52	BYTES	DATA	1	0
pulse	(4) CB2 high	CRB	60	BYTES	DATA	1	1

Delay 50 ms to allow pulse to take effect
Increment BYTES by 1
If BYTES = 256, make BYTES = 0, increment QUARTERS by 1 and proceed
with the program; otherwise jump back to routine above to
put next DATA in next address (in BYTES) and pulse it.
If QUARTERS <8, proceed to the routine below; otherwise STOP

Increment	(1) CA2 low	CRA	52	BYTES	DATA	0	1
IC2	(2) CA2 high	CRA	60	BYTES	DATA	1	1

Jump back to begin loading the next quarter-kilobyte of data.

seconds to program the whole EPROM. Port B is used to transfer data to the EPROM while Port A is used for the lower eight address lines. This allows 256 bytes to be programmed as the address (in the BYTES counter or variable) increases one step at a time from 0 to 255 (0000 0000 to 1111 1111). At the next increment of address beyond 255 a low pulse is sent to the IC4 by making CA2 low, then high. This increments the count on inputs A8 to A10 so that the next block of 256 bytes may then be loaded. BYTES is reset to zero (this happens automatically in a machine code program if a single byte is used as the BYTES counter). The machine code counter or BASIC variable called QUARTERS is incremented to count the number of quarter-kilobytes (256 bytes) which has been loaded. Note that the value in the *software* counter QUARTERS is the same as the value output by the *hardware* counter IC4. QUARTERS is merely keeping a record of how far IC4 has counted. This process continues, the count in IC4 (and QUARTERS) being incremented once for every 256 bytes, from 0 to 8 (000 to 111, ignoring output D).

Table 6.5 Checking the EPROM

BASE is the starting address of the block of RAM in which the original program is stored.
EPROM is the base address of the EPROM, when in the 'read' socket.
BYTES is a counter (register or BASIC variable) able to count to 2048

	Make BYTES = 0
A:	Read contents of BASE+BYTES
	Compare this with contents of EPROM+BYTES
	If they are unequal, display warning and STOP
	If they are equal, increment BYTES by 1
	If BYTES is less than 2048, jump back to A
	If BYTES = 2048, STOP

When the whole 2 K has been loaded, QUARTERS will next be incremented from 8 to 9 and the process is stopped. The EPROM is then fully programmed. It is transferred to the read-only sockets and a simple program (Table 6.5) is used to check that the program has been correctly loaded.

Project 7
Mains remote controller

One of the problems of controlling external equipment by computer is that it normally requires a system of wiring throughout the house from the computer to the controlled devices. When you want to move a device from one room to another the wiring must be altered. This project makes use of wiring which is already installed in your house — the power mains itself. Any device which plugs into the mains for power can also receive a signal from the computer to switch it on or off. Battery-powered equipment such as radio sets can also be controlled by this system. If you want to move a device from one room to another, you simply unplug the receiver from the mains socket, take in into the other room and plug it into the socket there.

Table 7.1 The project in brief

Function: A system for remotely controlling electrically powered devices, using the house mains wires as a transmission channel.

Interest: Household automation.

Power supply: +5 V regulated, 25 mA (two transmitters). Each receiver requires +9 V stabilized, 35 mA (depending on resistance of relay coil).

Address bus: 1 address for each controlled device.

Data bus: not required.

Control bus: $\overline{WR}$, $\overline{RD}$.

Connection: direct or through I/O device.

No. of i.c.s: 4 for one controlled device; 6 for two controlled devices.

Special points: I.c.s in receivers are CMOS. An oscilloscope is very helpful though not essential for tuning the circuits.

How it works

The micro is equipped with a high-frequency signal transmitter. This is capable of generating tone bursts which have a number of fixed frequencies in the range 100 kHz to 800 kHz. Each of the controlled devices responds to one or more of these frequencies. The tone burst is fed to the neutral line of the mains supply (Fig. 7.1) and is carried to all parts of the house. Unless the house or building is a very large one, the signal can be detected by a receiver which is connected to the neutral line. When the signal is received, and provided it is of the frequency to which the receiver has been tuned, the receiver operates a relay. This switches the controlled device on or off.

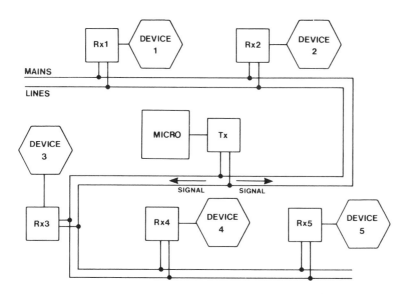

Fig. 7.1 Block diagram of a Mains Remote Control system (Tx = transmitter, Rx = receiver).

There are many different systems of mains remote control, some of which allow many more devices to be controlled. Some provide two-way communication so that information from the device can be fed back to the micro. However, these systems all involve circuitry of much greater complexity than the very simple and inexpensive one described in this project.

Let us look at the circuits in more detail, taking the transmitter first. Figure 7.2 shows a transmitter which generates a

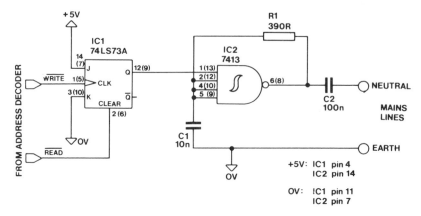

Fig. 7.2 Circuit diagram of the Mains Remote Control transmitter.

single frequency. You need a circuit like this for every device which is to be controlled. Its frequency is determined by the value of C1. The oscillator, based on a Schmitt trigger NAND gate (IC2), is enabled when the output from the flip-flop is made high. The flip-flop (IC1) is controlled by the output from the address decoder. Since the J input is wired to +5 V and the K input is wired to 0 V, the Q output takes the value of the J input whenever the clock input changes from high to low. Thus a low pulse on the WRITE line triggers the flip-flop, its Q output goes high and the oscillator is enabled. A low pulse on the READ line clears the flip-flop, its Q output goes low and the oscillator is disabled. These i.c.s contain two flip-flops and NAND gates. The pin numbers are given in brackets in Fig. 7.2, to show which connections to make should you be building a second transmitter.

The output from the oscillator is a square wave and with the values shown in Fig. 7.2 has a frequency of approximately 200 kHz. This is coupled to the neutral line of the mains supply by capacitor C2, a polypropylene capacitor with high working voltage. The neutral line is normallly very close to Earth potential but a fault in other electrical equipment could cause higher voltages to appear on the line temporarily. The receiver circuit (Fig. 7.3) is also coupled to the neutral line by a high-voltage capacitor (C3), and the signal is fed directly to a tone decoder i.c. By varying the setting of RV1, this circuit may be tuned to respond to a tone of particular frequency. With the values of C6, RV1 and RV2 shown in Fig. 7.3 it can be tuned to frequencies in the 200 kHz range. You may find it necessary to substitute a different resistor for R2 in order to tune it to other frequencies.

The frequency to which it is tuned is called the *centre frequency*. The i.c. responds to a range of frequencies on either side of the centre frequency. The band width of this response is determined by the value of the low-pass filter capacitor, C5. With the value given in Fig. 7.3, the bandwidth is about 16% at 200 kHz, so the tone decoder is triggered by signals with frequencies lying between about 170 and 230 kHz. If you are operating only a few devices on this system, it is possible to space the frequencies widely and have a relatively wide percentage bandwidth. This makes it easier to tune the decoder. If you require a narrower bandwidth to accommodate more devices, increase the value of C2 to 22 nF. This gives a bandwidth of approximately 8% at 200 kHz. Bandwidth decreases with frequency so at 400 kHz, for example, it is 8% and 4% respectively for the two values of C5 mentioned above. If you alter C5, alter C4 also, making it approximately twice the value of C5.

When no signal is being received, or there is a signal which is outside the range to which the circuit is tuned, the output at pin 8 is high (+9 V). As soon as a signal within the tuned range is received, the output drops sharply to 0 V and stays there for the duration of the signal. In this way the circuit picks out the particular frequency to which it is tuned, but ignores tone bursts

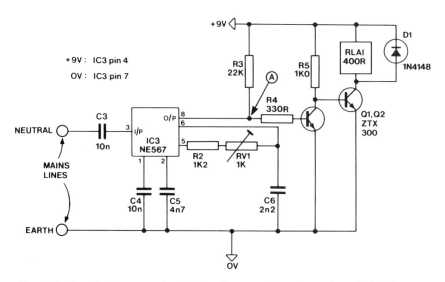

Fig. 7.3 Circuit diagram of a Mains Remote Control receiver. 'A' indicates where an optional flip-flop can be inserted (see Fig. 7.4).

intended for other tuned circuits. It also ignores all interference on the mains due to motors or other devices, and the a.c. frequency of the mains supply itself.

When the output of IC3 goes low, the transistor connected to this output through R4 is turned off. The potential at its collector rises sharply to +9 V. Base current begins to flow to the second transistor, turning it on. The relay is in the collector circuit of this transistor and its coil is energised. This causes the relay contacts (not shown in Fig. 7.3) to open or close, depending on the type of relay used. These switch on or off one or more electrically powered appliances.

The circuit in Fig. 7.3 energises the relay for as long as the signal is being received. If you have only one or two devices in the system and only one of these is required to be active at one time, it is a simple matter to arrange for the corresponding transmitter to send the tone continuously. If you want to be able to run several devices together and to have more than one switched on at any one time, the circuit may be modified as in Fig. 7.4. This shows a flip-flop which is connected between the output of IC1 and the transistors (i.e. at point A in Fig. 7.3). This flip-flop has similar inputs and outputs to that used in the transmitter (IC1, Fig. 7.2) but there are some important differences. A CMOS flip-flop has been chosen for the receiver, so that it may be operated on the 9 V supply. This type of flip-flop is triggered by a *rising* clock input whereas IC1 is triggered by a *falling* clock input.

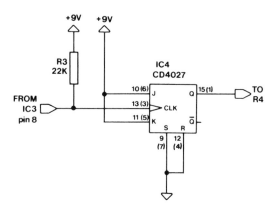

Fig. 7.4 Flip-flop circuit for producing a toggle action.

When a tone is decoded and the output of IC3 falls, there is no effect on IC4. When the tone ends, the output of IC3 rises, so triggering IC3. In the receiver, the J and K inputs of the flip-flop are both connected to +9 V. The result of this is that the output of the IC changes state every time it is triggered. This provides a toggling action. The relay changes at each burst of tone. The micro must send a tone burst to switch the device on and another burst to switch it off again. This simple circuit has the slight disadvantage that the micro has no means of knowing whether a given burst has turned the device on or off. The user must ensure that the device is in the correct state at the beginning of the program. The micro is programmed to keep a record of how many bursts have been transmitted. One further word of warning — if the mains is subject to heavy interference, or if there is an interruption of the power supply, it is possible that the receiver may be triggered into the opposite state from that registered in the computer. It is important to ensure that such an event can not lead to dangerous situations, such as electric heaters being switched on when they should be off.

Each controlled device needs its own receiver. Each receiver requires a 9 V stabilized power supply, though if several receivers are situated in the same room or adjacent rooms it is feasible to use one power supply for all of them. Figure 0.7(a) shows a circuit for a power supply suitable for a single receiver. Since a receiver requires only about 35 mA, low-rated components are used (see component list at the end of this project) and the circuit need occupy only a small volume. Power consumption reaches the full 35 mA only when the relay is activated. If you wish to fit a relay with a coil of smaller resistance, calculate the current the coil takes when energised and if necessary increase the rating of the components of the power supply circuit (including Q2) accordingly.

Planning the System

There are two main ways in which the system may be used. One way is to treat each controlled device individually, the other is to build a number of identical controlled power sockets into which each device is plugged as required.

The individual system can be tailored to the requirements of each device. A device might require two or more receivers for certain applications, each receiver operating on its own frequency. For example, a bedside radio set might be provided with a receiver and relay to turn it on and off and a relay wired into the loudspeaker circuit to give full or muted sound. At waking time, the radio would be switched on with muted volume. Five or ten minutes later the volume would be increased to its full level as a warning that 'snooze time' is over. The relays used here depend on the type of radio set. If the set is mains-powered, the relay for switching it on or off would be one able to work with mains voltage and a current of up to 1 A (though it would actually carry much less than this). Otherwise, it could be a low-voltage reed relay. The relay used in the volume control circuit (perhaps switching an additional resistor in series with the speaker) could be a light-duty type such as a reed relay. These can be obtained in the same d.i.l. package as integrated circuits, suitable for mounting on a circuit board. If the case of the set is large enough, mount the remote control receiver circuit and its 9 V power supply inside the case. It might even be feasible to use the 9 V power supply of the radio set, if it has one. Whether you are able to utilize this depends on your expertise with radio circuits.

A more straightforward approach is to build a number of remotely-controlled power outlets. Each consists of a case containing a receiver and its 9 V power supply. The mains lead is plugged into a convenient wall socket and may possibly be short, the case being mounted on the wall beside the wall socket. A power socket of conventional type is bolted to the case. Power is supplied to this socket by way of the relay, though the socket may also have its own built-in switch to override the remote-control action. Any mains-powered device may now be plugged into this socket and be remotely controlled by the frequency alloted to that socket. This system caters only for devices which are to be controlled by switching the mains power supply but it has the advantage of flexibility. A new device can be introduced to the system simply by plugging it in to one of the controlled sockets. The device itself is unaltered and can later be removed and used in the normal way in some other part of the house — or it can be transferred to another controlled socket.

Before beginning to build this project it is worth while considering carefully which kind of system you intend to implement.

Construction

IT IS ESSENTIAL THAT NO CONNECTION OF ANY KIND IS

MADE TO THE LIVE LINE OF THE MAINS. If there is any doubt about the correctness of the wiring of the mains supply, it is advisable to test it, using an electrician's screwdriver which has a live mains indicator lamp. Before making any connection to the mains outlet, check each terminal to ascertain which is the live one.

Begin by building the transmitter. It is advisable to leave spare space on the circuit board so that the system may be expanded at a later date. For a single-tone transmitter, located at a single address in memory, the address decoder has to supply both the $\overline{\text{WRITE}}$ and $\overline{\text{READ}}$ outputs (both active-low). Suitable logic circuits are given in Fig. 0.5. However, if you want to operate several transmitters, or may want to do so in the future, it is better to use a circuit such as that of Fig. 0.4. This has eight outputs corresponding to eight addresses in memory. Up to seven of these may be connected to the clock inputs of seven different transmitter circuits. The eighth output is connected to the clear inputs of all flip-flops. With this system, a write or read command to one of the first seven addresses triggers the corresponding transmitter to begin ending its tone. A moment later, a write or read command to the eighth address clears all flip-flops and the tone ceases. Clearing a flip-flop which is already in the cleared state has no effect on its output.

Each transmitter must oscillate at a different frequency. Figure 7.2 shows the values of C1 and R1 which give 200 kHz. In the other transmitters C1 and possibly R1 will have different values. If R1 is 390 ohms as shown, the approximate frequency of the oscillator may be calculated from the equation:

$$f = 200/C$$

where f is in hertz and C is in microfarads. By using single capacitors of different values and by using two or more capacitors in parallel it is easy to set up a number of different frequencies in the range 100 to 800 kHz. Slight adjustment of f may be made by altering R1 between 33 and 470 ohms. An oscilloscope may be used to measure the frequencies obtained. Before the transmitter is connected to the mains the signal is a sharp square wave with 5 V amplitude. When the connection to the mains has been made and the oscilloscope is connected to the mains side of C2 the signal may be more difficult to distinguish.

Provided that the usual precautions are taken to exclude the possibility of mains voltages appearing where they should not be (see p. 18), the receiver circuit and its 9 V power supply may be built on the same board. Build the power supply and then wire up IC1 and its associated components.

The receiver may be tested without connecting it to the mains lines. Run a wire from the output of the transmitter to the input of the receiver, and join their Earth terminals by a second wire. Connect a voltmeter or oscilloscope probe to pin 8 of IC3, and switch on the power. The voltage at pin 8 will probably be +9 V, since it is unlikely that the circuit will be already tuned to the correct frequency. Adjust RV1 *very slowly*, until a point is found at which the output drops to 0 V. Even with a wide bandwidth it needs careful adjustment to find the right setting.

RV1 has been given a low value so that the correct setting may be more easily found, but it may happen that owing to tolerance variations in capacitor C6 it is impossible to find the right setting over the whole range of RV1. In this event, replace R2 with a resistor of higher or lower value. It will help you find the correct setting for RV1 if you use an oscilloscope to monitor the waveform at pin 5. Adjust RV1 until this has the same frequency as the transmitter. The point at which output drops to 0 V will be found with a little further readjustment of RV1.

If you require toggle action, build the flip-flop circuit (Fig. 7.4) and connect this to the output of IC3. If only one of the flip-flops in IC4 is being used, it is essential that unused inputs of the other flip-flop are connected to +9 V (or 0 V), as listed in Table 7.2. There should be no problem in getting this part of the circuit to operate.

Table 7.2 Connections not shown in Figs 7.2 to 7.4

	To 0 V	To +5 V	To +9 V
IC1	pin 11	pins 4, 5–7*, 10*	—
IC2	pin 7	pins 9*, 10*, 12* 13*, 14	
IC3	pin 7	—	pin 4
IC4	pin 8	—	pins 3–7*, 16

* If the second gate or flip-flop is not used.

Table 7.3 Components required for each transmitter

Resistor

R1   390R (or 330R or 470R, see text), carbon,
         0.25 W, 5% tolerance

Capacitors

C1   10n polyester (or similar values, see text)
C2   100n polypropylene, 1000 V d.c. working

Integrated circuits

IC1   74LS73A dual J–K flip-flops, with clear
IC2   7413 dual 4-input Schmitt trigger NAND gates
These may be shared between two transmitters

Miscellaneous

Circuit board
14-pin i.c. sockets (2 off)
Edge-connectors or other multiway plugs, with ribbon cable for connection
to micro (2 ways plus 8 or 16 address lines)
Mains-type plug
Components for making address decoder (see p. 7)

Finally wire the transistors and relay. Check that the contacts
of the relay are rated to switch current of the magnitude intended.
As a final bench test, switch on the power to transmitter and receiver. The relay is energised for as long as the tone is being transmitted or, if you have incorporated the flip-flop of Fig. 7.4 the
relay changes state at the end of each tone burst. This test may be
repeated with the output of the transmitter connected to the
neutral mains line and the receiver similarly attached in another
room. It operates just as reliably under these circumstances and is
normally unaffected by other applicances such as refrigerators and
washing machines being run at the same time.

Programming

There is little to say on this subject, since all that has to be done is
to POKE or PEEK the address of the appropriate transmitter. If
you are using toggle-action, program the micro to deliver a tone
burst lasting about 1 second. This gives the decoder plenty of time
to detect the signal and respond to it.

Table 7.4 Components required for each receiver

Resistors (carbon, 0.25 W, 5% tolerance)

R2	1k2 (or other values, see text)
R3	22k
R4	330R
R5	1k0
RV1	1k0, variable preset resistor

Capacitors

C3	10n, polypropylene, 1000 V d.c. working
C4	10n, disc ceramic
C5	4n7, disc ceramic
C6	2n2, polystyrene

Semiconductors

D1	1N4148 or similar silicon diode
Q1, Q2	ZTX300 or similar npn transistor (2 off)

Integrated circuits

IC3	NE567 tone-decoder/phase-locked-loop i.c.
IC4	CD4027BE dual J–K flip-flops with set and reset (required for toggle action only)

Miscellaneous

Circuit board
8-pin i.c. socket
16-pin i.c. socket (for flip-flop)
Mains-type plug
RLA1   relay, type according to voltage and current to be switched and contacts according to switching required (see text)

The Real Time Clock (Project 2) or the Alarm Clock Timer (Project 12) are ideal accessories to a mains remote control system. With their aid you can program the micro to perform all sorts of routine operations automatically. It can wake you in the morning by turning on the bedside radio and possibly an electric coffee-maker. You can also program it to switch on favourite radio or TV programs throughout the day. It can switch on the porch light at nights and activate the security system at bedtime.

Table 7.5 Components required for 9 V power supply (see Fig. 0.7a)

Resistor

R1   82R, carbon, 0.25W, 5% tolerance

Capacitors

C1, C2   220μ, 16 V working, electrolytic (2 off)

Semiconductors

D1–D4   1 A rectifier diodes or 1 A bridge
D5   BZY88C, 9V1, zener diode
Q1   ZTX300 npn transistor

Miscellaneous

Circuit board
T1   Mains transformer 12 V, 1.2 VA, circuit-board mounting type
S1   SPST switch, mains rated
FS1   100mA fuse and holder
Mains lead and plug

Project 8
Voice-operated controller

Talking to your micro and making it obey your spoken commands can easily be achieved with this device. It is simple to build and operate, and the cost of the components is low, so do not expect that it will give the micro an extensive vocabulary. Nevertheless, with a little ingenuity on your part, it is possible to compile a useful collection of words and phrases which the micro is able to interpret reliably. It can be fun teaching the micro to understand what you tell it!

Table 8.1 The project in brief

Function: Controlling the micro by spoken words or other sound signals.
Interest: Robotics, disabled persons, model control, security systems, micro-computer enthusiasts generally.
Power supplies: +5 V d.c. regulated, 15mA.
Address bus: 1 address.
Data bus: 2 lines.
Control bus: not required.
Connections: direct or through an I/O.
No. of i.c.s: 4.
Special point: IC1 and IC2 are CMOS.

Part of the circuit also detects the frequency of musical or semi-musical sounds. The output from this section may be used to make the micro respond to sounds of given pitch. It can be programmed to respond when you whistle to it, the response depending on the pitch of the note or the sequence of notes. In conjunction with the Music Generator (Project 5) you could whistle a tune and have the micro play it back to you.

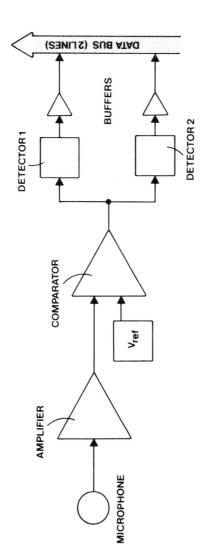

Fig. 8.1 Block diagram of the Voice-operated Controller.

How it works

Figure 8.1 shows the main section of the circuit. Sound is picked up by a microphone. The e.m.f. from the microphone is amplified. It is sensitive to the spoken voice, even when the microphone is several metres away. The output from the amplifier is fed to a comparator. This compares the amplifier output with a reference voltage. The voltage is set to be just a little higher than that from the amplifier when there is no sound. The output from the comparator is then low (very close to +0 V). The slightest sound causes the output from the amplifier to rise and fall. As it falls below the reference voltage, the output from the comparator rises abruptly to +5 V. As can be seen from Fig. 8.2, the comparator (IC2) is an operational amplifier with no feedback. Consequently it has exceedingly high gain, and rapidly becomes saturated in either direction, making its output swing sharply between 0 V and +5 V. The effect of this is to convert the input from the microphone (above a given threshold, depending on the reference voltage at RV1) into a square wave. The square wave has the same frequency as the original sound.

The circuit may be made less sensitive by adjusting RV1, to reduce the reference voltage. This may be necessary in a noisy environment. You may need to hold the microphone fairly close to your mouth and speak loudly under such circumstances.

The output from the comparator goes to two level detectors. Detector 1 is simply a Schmitt trigger NAND gate wired as an inverter. Since the voltage input to it is already swinging fully between 0 V and +5 V this gate merely inverts that voltage, giving a square wave of the same frequency as the original sound.

Detector 2 includes an integrating circuit. When a sound is made and the output of the comparator swings high, a current flows through the diode. This charges the storage capacitor C1. The longer the output is high, the more current flows and the greater the voltage produced across the capacitor. C1 discharges slowly through R7, but when the output of the comparator returns to zero, the diode prevents it from being discharged rapidly. The result is that the level of charge on C1 depends mainly on the duration of the sound. There is a double effect, for the louder the sound the greater its amplitude. With a louder sound, the output of the amplifier is below the threshold for a bigger proportion of the time. As a result, the output of the comparator is high for a bigger proportion of the time, increasing the voltage across C1.

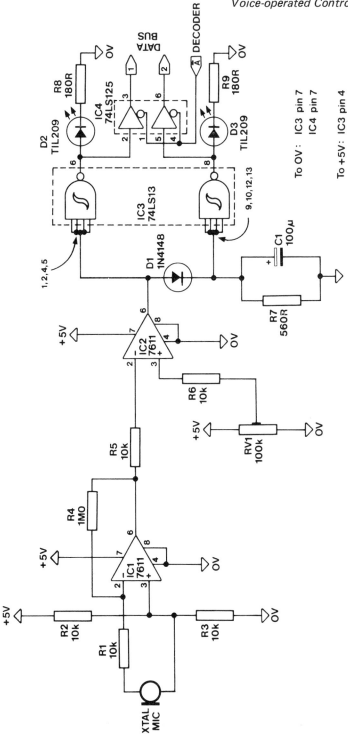

Fig. 8.2 Circuit diagram of the Voice-operated Controller.

The level of voltage on C1 is detected by the other Schmitt trigger NAND gate. When the voltage across C1 is low, the output of the gate is high. As the level rises the output of the gate falls to 0 V.

The circuit includes two LEDs to indicate the state of each detector. These LEDs are not essential for operating the circuit with a micro, but to visualise the outputs helps you to understand what happens as you pronounce a word or phrase. This in turn helps you to design the program that the micro needs for interpreting the sounds.

When there is no sound, both LEDs are lit. As soon as a sound is made, LED1 begins to flicker. In fact, it is flickering at audio frequency, which is too fast for the eye to follow, but irregularities in the waveforms cause an overall flickering effect. With sounds of short duration, or low volume, or which lack 'explosive' content, LED2 remains lit. With louder sounds, particularly voiced sounds which are 'explosive' (for example, the 'p' at the end of 'stop'), LED2 goes out. The length of time LED2 is out depends on the nature of the word (i.e. its volume, accented syllables, 'explosiveness') and the length of time taken to pronounce it. With a phrase of two or three words, the LED may go on and off several times for periods of differing lengths. It is by analysing the timing of the output from Detector 2 (LED2) and the steadiness or unsteadiness (LED1 flickering) of the output from Detector 1 that the micro is able to distinguish between various words or phrases. If the micro is programmed to find the frequency of the output from Detector 1 it is able to respond to notes of different pitch.

Construction

The project uses two CMOS operational amplifiers, so the usual precautions should be taken when handling these (p. 22). The main reason for choosing the 7611 for this project is that it requires only a small supply voltage. Another advantage is its low current consumption (1 mA each i.c.).

It is best to build and test each stage, beginning with the amplifier (IC1). Note that pin 8 of both IC1 and IC2 are to be wired to the 0 V line. The output from the amplifier is about +2.5 V in the absence of sound. A voice of average volume about 10 cm from

Table 8.2 Components Required

Resistors (carbon, 0.25 W, 5% tolerance)

R1–R3, R5–R6	10k (5 off)
R2	1M0
R7	560R
R8, R9	180R (2 off)
RV1	100k, preset potentiometer

Capacitor

C1	100 μF electrolytic

Semiconductors

D1	1N4148 silicon diode
D2, D3	TIL209 or similar light-emitting diode (2 off)

Integrated circuits

IC1, IC2	7611 CMOS operational amplifiers (2 off)
IC3	74LS13 dual 4-input Schmitt trigger NAND gates
IC4	74LS125 quadruple bus buffer gates, with three-state outputs

Miscellaneous

Circuit board
8-pin i.c. sockets (2 off)
14-pin i.c. sockets (2 off)
Crystal microphone, or microphone insert, with cable
Edge-connector or multiway plug with ribbon cable for connections to
micro (4 ways plus 8 or 16 address lines)
Components for making address decoder (see p. 7)

---

the microphone produces a signal with a peak-to-peak amplitude of about 20 mV. The diagram shows that RV2 is a preset resistor, but if you are likely to want to alter the sensitivity of the device, fit a volume-control potentiometer in place of this, and mount it on the panel of the enclosure.

When IC2 has been wired, its output may be measured with a voltmeter if an oscilloscope is not available. Position RV1 so that the wiper is toward the 0 V end of the track. The output of IC2 is 0 V. Slowly turn RV1 until the output suddenly swings to +5 V, then turn it *very slightly* in the opposite direction, until the output swings back to 0 V again. With this setting, the output of IC2 is 0 V in the absence of sound, but swings high when even a small sound is made. The room must be as quiet as possible while this critical adjustment is being made. The output of IC2 swings violently between high and low when any sound is made. With a voltmeter, this will show as a slight trembling of the needle, but with an oscilloscope you will be able to see a square wave-form of the same frequency as the original sound.

Finally build and test the detectors. The output from Detector 1 (IC3, pin 6) is the inverse of the output of IC2. The other detector may be tested by measuring the voltage at the junction of D1 and C1. This is 0 V in the absence of sound. When a sound is made, the voltage rises slowly. It reaches 5 V only if the sound is prolonged, loud or 'explosive'. As it rises above 1.6 V the output of the gate (IC3, pin 8) swings from +5 V to 0 V. Since this is a Schmitt trigger there is hysteresis and the output does not revert to 0 V until the input voltage falls below about 0.8 V. This feature eliminates the possibility of obtaining a rapidly oscillating output with a slowly rising input voltage such as this.

The LEDs are best mounted side by side on the panel of the enclosure.

If the circuit is to be connected to the micro through an I/O device, the buffers (IC4) are not required. The outputs from IC1 may be taken directly to two lines (such as PA1 and PA2) of one of the ports. If the circuit is to be connected to the data bus, the buffers are required, as shown in Fig. 8.2. It is also necessary to build an address decoder. Since this is a 'read-only' circuit, there is no need to use the $\overline{\text{RD}}$ control line.

Programming

The device provides two outputs, on data lines D1 and D2. D1 is normally '1' but alternates between '1' and '0' at audio frequency whenever there is sound. D2 is normally '1' and changes to '0' for the duration of the louder and more forceful sounds. The simplest approach to programming is to choose a set of spoken commands that you would like the computer to obey and see what effects they produce when spoken. The LEDs help you to see how different words and phrases affect the outputs. For example, the word 'stop' produces a flickering of LED1 (alternate high and low on D1) during the first part of the word ('sto . . .'). LED2 goes out at the final explosive 'p'. By contrast, LED2 goes out at the very beginning of the word 'go', and remains off during the whole word.

It is instructive to pronounce a series of similar words and syllables to observe their effects. For example, the words 'go', 'no', 'to', 'ho', 'lo', etc. do not give identical results, so it is easy to program the micro to distinguish between many of these.

Enthusiastic programmers will find plenty of interest in compiling lists of commands and then writing a program which instructs the micro to identify each command reliably.

Figure 8.3 is the flow-chart of a program to obtain the essential information. The reader will probably want to expand this after a certain amount of experimenting with the Controller. Both data lines are read at the same time, so there are four possible values:

'11' (decimal 3)   means *either* silence *or* that there is sound (not loud) with D1 temporarily high

'10' (decimal 2)   means that there is sound, (but not loud)

'01' (decimal 1)   means that there is loud sound, D1 high

'00' (decimal 0)   also means loud sound, D1 low

The program of Fig. 8.3 requires three registers or variables to record counts, which are the rough equivalents of lengths of time:

TIME0   length of silence
TIME1   length of sound, but not loud sound
TIME2   length of loud sound

The counts are stored in a 2-dimensional array. One dimension covers TIME1 and TIME2. The other dimension covers the individual phases of the sound. The program reads data continuously and increments TIME0 whenever the data equals 3. If there are 500 such readings consecutively it may be assumed that output 1 is not alternating so there is silence. Whenever the data is other than 3, either TIME1 or TIME2 are incremented.

A register or variable called PHASE keeps count of the number of phases in any sequence of sound. A phase lasts for 500 counts of TIME0. At the end of each phase, the contents of the TIME1 and TIME2 are transferred to the array. The number in PHASE is incremented so that the next set of values in the TIME registers are transferred to the next row of the array. If it is found that TIME1 and TIME2 are both zero, there has been a significantly long period of silence, and the spoken command can be taken as complete. The program jumps to a subroutine which analyses the contents of the array, and performs the actions which the analysis

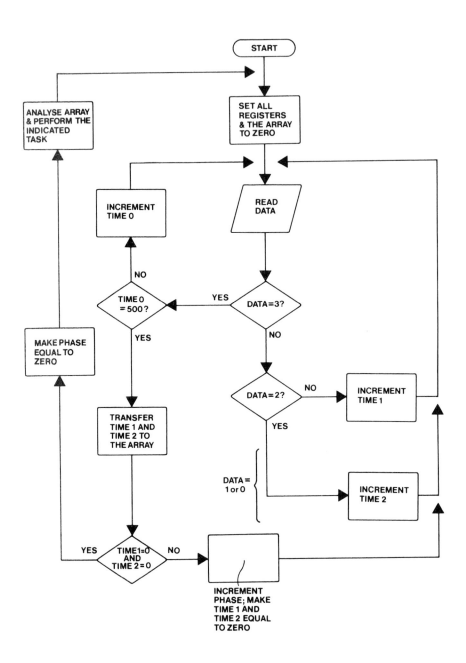

Fig. 8.3 Flow-chart of a program for using the Voice-operated Controller
to analyse a spoken word.

indicates. Then it clears the arrays, resets all registers or variables and returns to the start of the program.

The analytical routines become complicated if you have a long list of commands, so it is best to begin with a small list and add others later, if required. It is not possible to give a detailed program here, but an example will explain the general procedure. Suppose that there are just four commands: 'Stop', 'Go', 'Turn left' and 'Turn right'. Depending on how the words are pronounced, the last two might have similar effects on the Controller but, by holding the word 'right' for longer that the word 'left', it is possible to help the micro to resolve these two phrases. The program should also be able to differentiate between spoken commands and other noises that the microphone is likely to pick up.

At analysis of the word 'Stop', the contents of the array might look like this:

Phase	TIME1	TIME2	Interpretation
0	250	0	Initial 'Sto . .'
1	250	0	Continued
2	250	400	'p'
3	70	150	'p'
4	0	0	Word finished

This shows a period of sound terminating in an explosive 'p'.
By contrast, the word 'Go' might give:

Phase	TIME1	TIME2	Intepretation
0	250	500	Initial 'G'
1	250	500	'o', dying out
2	30	300	still dying
3	0	0	Word finished

This has only 3 phases, for the word is spoken more rapidly than 'Stop'; also, it is a more 'powerful' word and Detector 2 takes longer to settle after the sound has finished.

The other commands would have more phases with TIME2 showing initial high values, then low ones (between words) followed by high ones. Extension of the pronunciation of the word 'right' will certainly identify it, if no other difference is apparent from the array.

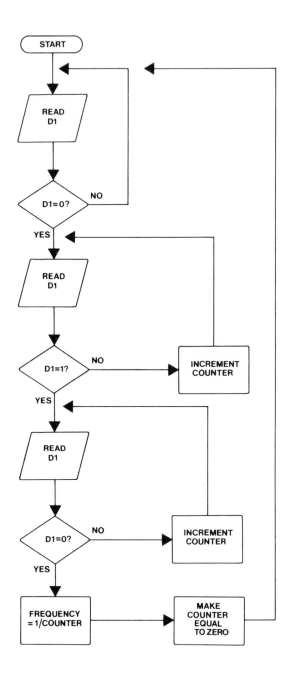

Fig. 8.4 Flow-chart of a program for using the Voice-operated Controller to measure the frequency of a note.

Since the output of Detector 1 has the frequency of the original sound, a program which measures this frequency is a further aid to analysis. It can be used with words spoken or 'half-sung'. The last part of the word 'Go', for example, can be spoken with a definite pitch which is detectable by a program such as that shown in Fig. 8.4. This program gives a fairly accurate measure of frequency and so is applicable when commands are issued by means of whistling. For greatest accuracy the program should be written in machine code.

Project 9
Sound processor

This project has many serious uses but it provides a lot of fun too. It comprises of an analogue-to-digital converter and a digital-to-analogue converter. Figure 9.1 shows what the converters do in this device. The A-to-D converter receives audio signals from a signal source, which might be a tape recorder, a radio set, or an audio amplifier with a microphone connected to it. The analogue voltage is converted into digital form and can be read by the computer by way of the data bus. The converter works at very high speed, converting the signal about 28 000 times each second. The micro reads the digital signal at about the same rate. The need for high-speed reading explains why the micro must be programmed in machine code.

Table 9.1 The project in brief

Function: Converts analogue sound signals to digital form, for processing by microcomputer. After this, they are converted back to analogue sound signals. Used to provide delays, echoes, digital filtering, and many other effects. Also for frequency analysis.

Interest: Hi-fi and audio, musicians, experimenters.

Power supplies: +5 V d.c. regulated, 60 mA; −5 V to −30 V d.c., 65 μA; +12 V to +20 V d.c., 0.5 to 1 A (for power amplifier, separate power pack advised).

Address bus: 1 address

Data bus: 8 bits

Control bus: Read and write.

Connection: Direct connection preferred.

No. of i.c.s.: 11.

Special points: IC6 is CMOS (see p. 22). Machine-code programming essential.

The micro may be programmed to process the digital signals in many and varied ways, as will be explained later. Even short

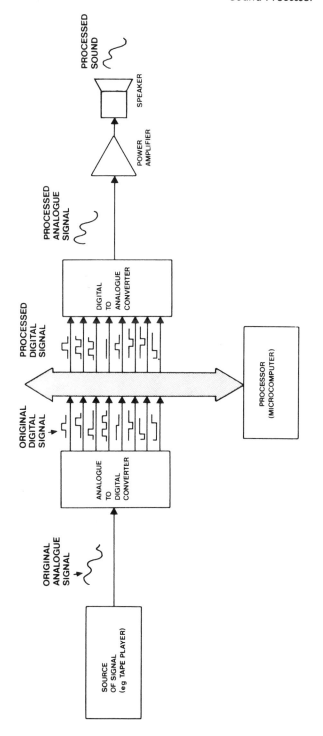

Fig. 9.1 Block diagram of the Sound Processor.

programs can provide really fascinating sound effects.

In between reading digital signals, the micro is writing their processed values to the other section of the device, the digital-to-analogue converter. The output from this is an analogue audio frequency voltage, the processed analogue signal. The waveform of this is related to the original waveform in a way determined by the processing the micro has done. This signal is sent to an audio amplifier and is then heard as sound, from a loudspeaker.

The idea of taking a sound signal, converting it to digital form, processing it and then converting it back to analogue form again is a very simple one to grasp and might seem to be rather a pointless operation. The interest of this device lies in the things we can do with the signal while it is being operated on by the micro. The possibilities include:

Delay

The micro reads sample values and stores them in sequence in memory. In between reading each sample, it takes a previously stored value and writes this to the D-to-A converter. The samples are sent out in the same order as they were received but after a fixed delay.

Echo and reverberation

Samples are read and stored, as above. Each sample is sent out immediately but, before it is sent out, a fraction of the value of an earlier sample (taken from memory) is added to it. For example, the program might sum the sample with one quarter of the value of a sample received 1 second earlier. It sends the sum to the D-to-A converter. We hear the sound plus a faint echo of the sound already heard one second earlier. Processing in this way gives just a single echo. If the computer is programmed to store the sum instead of storing the original signal, we get a repeated echo, gradually dying away. Similar processing with shorter time intervals gives reverberation.

Filtering

The essence of this operation is that a fraction of each new sample is summed with a fraction of the previous sample. The sum is sent to the converter. It works like this:

Previous sample Y	New sample X	Sum Y/2 + X/2 (*sent out*)
128	140	134
134	144	139
139	151	145
145	143	144

At each stage the sum sent out becomes the 'previous sample' for the next stage. In this example we take half of X and of Y, so that the sum is actually the average of the two. We can take any pair of fractions we like, provided the fractions total 1 (e.g. $\frac{1}{4}$Y + $\frac{3}{4}$X, or $\frac{1}{20}$Y + $\frac{19}{20}$X). The effect of this processing is dependent on frequency. Rapid (i.e. high-frequency) changes in value do not have a significant effect on the signals. They are averaged out with previous values. A sudden large increase followed by a sudden large decrease in value is lost almost immediately. Only slow long-term (low-frequency) changes are effective in changing the output value. As a result, high frequencies are reduced, and the program acts as a *low-pass filter*. It is the software equivalent of the conventional resistor-capacitor low-pass filter.

If we reverse the sign of the previous output before adding a small fraction of it to a large fraction of the current signal, we obtain the reverse effect. In this case the sum is aX − bY (where a + b = 1, as before and a > b). The outgoing signal is composed mainly of the most recent sample (aX). The influence of earlier samples is rapidly removed by subtraction of bY. Long-term trends die out quickly and short-term changes are retained. We have a *high-pass filter*. It is possible to combine the above computations so that the micro acts as a *band-pass filter*, or as a *notch filter*. All kinds of exotic filters may be realized by summing various combinations of fractions of previous of signals. From sepulchral groans to Mickey-Mouse squeakings, there is no end to what can be done with digital filters.

Other effects

If your micro has sufficient RAM to store a long sequence of sample values, you can program it to play them back in various ways. Sending them out in reverse order is an obvious example. Try sending out alternate values only, to double the tempo of music without changing pitch, or send each value twice. Capture the waveforms of a clarinet playing each note of the scale, then program the micro to play these different notes when different keys are pressed. This gives you a computer organ with the timbre of a clarinet. Attack and decay may not be quite right, but the effect is certain to be unusual.

Fourier analysis

Waveforms may be stored and then analysed. The analysis will tell you which frequencies are dominant in the sound. You can use Fourier analysis on recorded bird song, for example, or write a program to recognise the voices of your friends.

How it works

The first stage is the conversion of the analogue signal (V) to its digital equivalent. It is essential that an audio signal is sampled at a rate which is at least double the highest frequency we wish to cover. With this circuit a complete sampling cycle lasts 35 μs, giving about 28 000 samples per second. Thus, the highest frequency which the system can deal with is about 14 kHz. The converter circuit has been designed so that it operates continuously. The rate at which the micro reads the output from the converter depends solely on the timing of its program. If it reads very fast it may read the same sample twice. If it reads slowly, it may miss out samples. The main point is that there is no attempt to synchronise the converter and the micro. This means that programming is simpler, since there is no need to send control signals to the converter. The micro just reads the data bus and accepts any signal which happens to be put on to it at that time. This asynchronous operation also ensures that the circuit will work with any model of micro.

The audio signal comes from an audio amplifier. It should have a maximum amplitude of 2.5 V peak-to-peak. The 'earphone' output of any domestic tape recorder or radio set is suitable. The amplifier is coupled to the converter circuit by C1 (Fig. 9.5). R1 and R2 bias the quiescent (no signal) voltage to 1.25 V, so that the input to IC1 ranges between 0 V and 2.5 V. IC1 converts this signal to a digital value in the range 0 to 255. Figure 9.2 shows what happens. On the left of the figure we see the voltage levels of the original analogue signal and their digital equivalents. The quiescent voltage gives a digital output of about 128. The figure shows the results of three successive conversions. Instead of an analogue voltage falling smoothly from 2.25 to 0.825 V, we have three digital samples, expressed in decimal for convenience as 230, 173 and 84. These are read by the micro and processed in one of the ways described above. If the analogue signal had a high-frequency ripple superimposed on its smooth fall, this would be missed. We would need to increase the sampling frequency to detect this.

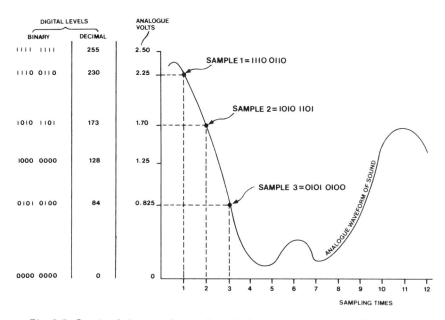

Fig. 9.2 Graph of the waveform of original analogue sound signal, showing how it is sampled at intervals. The figures on the left illustrate the three ways of representing the levels and samples.

The main sections of the analogue-to-digital converter (IC1) are shown in Fig. 9.3. Its operation centres on an 8-bit register. When the 'start conversion' command has been given (by low pulse at the SC input) the most significant bit of the register is set to '1', the other bits being set to '0'. This puts the value '128' in the register. The outputs of the register control 8 analogue voltage switches which operate an R-2R ladder. The way such a ladder works has been described in Project 5 (see Fig. 5.2).

The switches connect the 'rungs' of the ladder to 0 V or to V_{ref}, producing an output voltage V_L in that range. When the register holds '128' the output voltage is $V_{ref}/2$. The comparator compares V_L with V_{in}. If V_{in} is less than V_L (i.e. V_{in} is less than

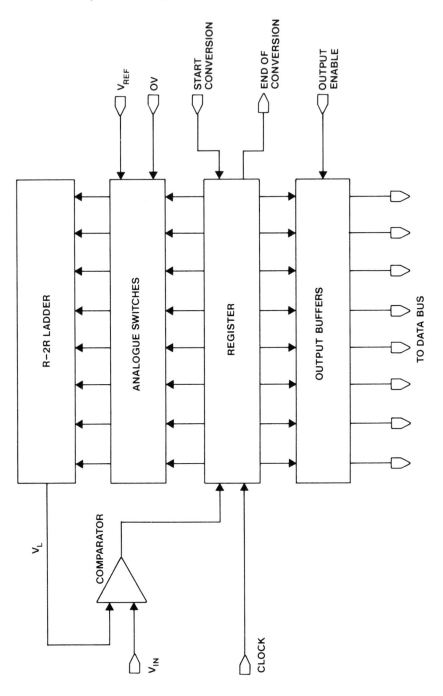

Fig. 9.3 Simplified block diagram of the analogue-to-digital converter i.c.

$V_{ref}/2$), the most significant bit is made '0'. Otherwise it retains its value '1'. Thus it has been established whether V_{in} lies in the top half of the range or the bottom half.

Now, the next most significant bit is made '1'. If V_{in} is less than $V_{ref}/2$ the value in the register will be '0100 0000' and V_L will be $V_{ref}/4$. The comparator now decides whether V_{in} lies in the upper or lower half of the lower half of the voltage range. On the other hand, if V_{in} is more than $V_{ref}/2$, the value in the register will be '1100 0000' and V_L will be $3 \times V_{ref}/4$. The comparator decides whether V_{in} lies in the upper or lower half of the upper voltage range.

This process is repeated at each clock pulse, gradually bringing V_L closer toward V_{in}. This is known as successive approximation.

After eight clock pulses, the least significant bit has been determined and conversion is complete. The register now holds an 8-bit value between 0 and 255 which represents the value of V_{in} to the nearest half bit. The 'end of conversion' output goes high. A high level at the 'output enable' input causes the values held in the register to be transferred to the data bus or, in this circuit, to the latches of IC2. If the 'end of conversion' output is wired directly to the 'output enable' as in this circuit, the result of each conversion is automatically sent to the latches.

Figure 9.4 shows the waveforms which are needed to control the converter. The NAND gate of IC5 is wired as an oscillator with a frequency of about 900 kHz. Its output is fed to a counter (IC6) which divides it by 2, 4, 8, 16 and 32, giving the waveforms Q1, Q2, Q3, Q4, and Q5 respectively. These are NANDed together by the 8-input NAND gate of IC7, which has a low output only when all of its inputs (Q1 to Q5) are high. This output is used to supply a short low pulse (SC) to the 'start conversion' input of the converter. For proper operation of the converter, this pulse should coincide with a negative clock pulse. For this reason Q1 is inverted by IC11 before being sent to the clock input of IC1. When SC goes low, the 'end of conversion' output goes low, indicating that conversion is under way. After nine clock pulses the conversion is complete (there is an initial period of up to one pulse to allow voltage levels to settle) and EOC goes high again. This causes the new data to appear at the outputs of the converter.

The clock input of the latch i.c. (IC2) is controlled by ANDing Q3 with Q5 (IC8 and IC11). The resulting waveform is shown at the bottom of Fig. 9.4. The latches operate on a rising edge, so data is transferred from the converter to the latches at the point marked on the figure. The new data is held in the latches and a few clock periods later a new conversion begins. The complete cycle takes 32 clock periods, which at 900 kHz gives a 28 000 conversions per second.

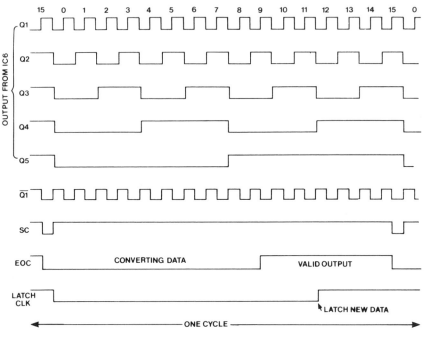

Fig. 9.4 The logical waveforms used for controlling the A-to-D converter and the latch.

Whenever the computer performs a 'read' operation, the data in the latches is fed through the three-state buffers (IC3) to the data bus.

Figure 9.5 shows what becomes of the three samples from Fig. 9.2 after they have been processed by the micro. In this example we are assuming that the processing has *not* altered their values. Each sample comes in turn from the micro and is written to the D-to-A converter (IC9). The operation of this has already been described under Project 5. For digital inputs in the range 0 to 255 it produces an output in the range 0 V to 2.5 V. Conversion begins whenever a low pulse is applied to its enable ($\overline{\text{EN}}$) input. This is provided by the $\overline{\text{WRITE}}$ output from the enabling circuit. Conversion takes about 0.8 μs. The output is latched so that once $\overline{\text{EN}}$ is made high (i.e. the write operation is complete), the voltage is held steady until the next write operation. The fact that other data may appear on the bus between one write operation and the next has no effect on the output.

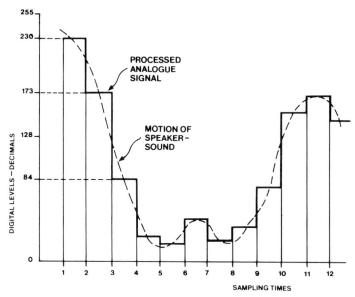

Fig. 9.5 Showing how an analogue signal is reconstituted from a succession of digitally-produced voltage levels.

The voltage from IC9 does not change smoothly, as did the original voltage, but is stepped. Since there are 256 possible values in the range 0 to 2.5 V, the minimum step is a rise or fall of 9.7 mV. The cone of the loudspeaker is driven to move in a stepped fashion too, but the effects of air resistance and inertia due to its mass will smooth out much of this. The result is a reasonably smooth waveform which, to our ears at least, is indistinguishable from a smooth waveform such as the original. If you compare Fig. 9.5 with Fig. 9.2 you will see that the original waveform has been re-created more-or-less exactly. For greater precision it would be necessary to increase the sampling rate and the number of bits per sample. Such refinements might be worth while for equipment used in a hi-fi recording studio but are unnecessary here.

IC10 is a conventional audio power amplifier i.c. It could be replaced with any of a variety of types, or even by a ready-built audio amplifier. This i.c. can operate on any supply voltage from +6 to +20 V. The amount of current required is relatively high and it is unlikely that the supply of the micro could provide this. A separate supply is therefore essential (see p. 19 for suitable circuits).

Construction

There are few discrete components, so the whole circuit can be accommodated on a board about 10 cm square. If you are soldering and not used to working in a confined space, use a slightly larger board. It is feasible to build the amplifier circuit (IC10 and its associated components) on a separate board. In a circuit as complicated as this one it is advisable to build and test each section before proceeding to the next. The order of construction is suggested below.

Clock and counter circuit (Fig. 9.6)

Insert IC6 in its socket *after* all wiring of this section is finished. If you have an oscilloscope, observe the outputs from IC11 pins 2 and 8, and IC7 pin 8, to check that they conform to Fig. 9.4. If the clock is running much too fast or slow, adjust the rate by substituting a resistor of lower or higher value for R6. The value of R6 *must* lie between 330Ω and 470Ω. If such adjustment is not enough, you will need to replace C3 with one of a different value. R7 is a pull-up resistor to interface the TTL i.c. to the CMOS i.c. and plays no part in the timing.

Table 9.2 Connections not shown in Figs 9.6 and 9.7

	To 0 V	To +5 V
IC2	pin 10	pin 20
IC3	pin 7	pin 14
IC4	pin 7	pin 14
IC5	pin 7	pins 1, 2, 4, 5, 14
IC6	pin 8	pin 16
IC7	pin 7	pin 14
IC8	pin 7	pins 4, 5, 9, 10, 12–14
IC11	pin 7	pins 3, 5, 11, 13, 14

A-to-D circuit (Fig. 9.6)

The quiescent voltage at the junction of R1 and R2 should be about 1.25 V. Since the current through R5 is about 65 μA (anything between 25 μA and 150 μA will do), the p.d. across it is 5.33 V and the voltage at pin 5 of IC1 should be 0.33 V. If your micro provides a different negative voltage in the range −5 to −30 V, you may use this supply instead. Select the nearest preferred value for R5 so as to give a current of about 65 μA when the voltage at pin 5 is about 0 V.

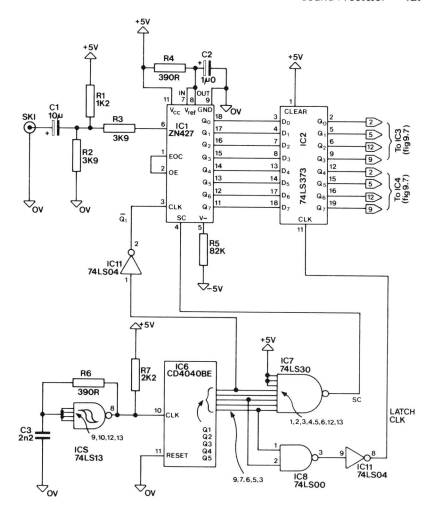

Fig. 9.6 Circuit diagram of the Sound Processor: the A-to-D converter and its associated i.c.s.

Address decoder and buffer circuit (Fig. 9.7)

See page 13 for a suitable address decoder circuit. *Wire* its READ output to IC3 and IC4.

The analogue input section is now complete and may be tested on the micro. The PEEK command of BASIC, or its equivalent in other high-level languages, is suitable for preliminary testing, though you can use a machine-code program if you prefer. With nothing connected to the input (SK1), PEEK should return a value close to 128. Next connect a potentiometer as in Fig. 9.8. Turn the wiper to the 0 V end of the track. PEEK should return

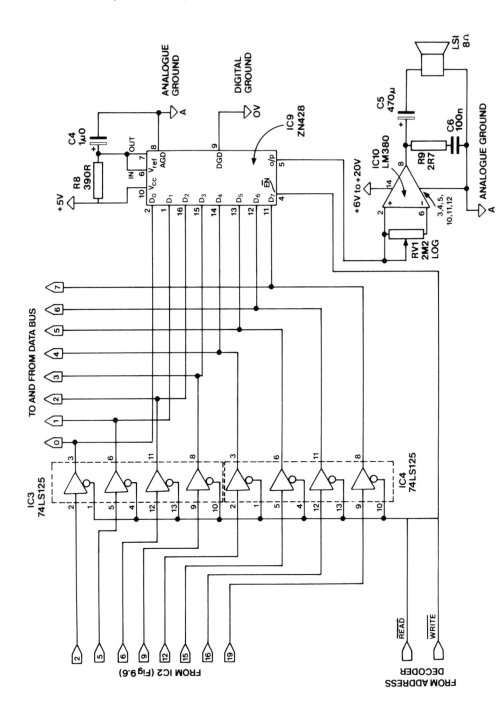

Fig. 9.7 Circuit diagram of the Sound Processor: the D-to-A converter and its associated i.c.s.

the value 0. Turn the wiper to the +5 V end. PEEK should return a value greater than 245, preferably 255. This circuit relies on the accuracy of the internal voltage reference of IC1 so it is possible that the values very close to 255 may not be obtained. This is not a serious matter in this application. Try various other settings of the wiper and see that you obtain appropriate values between 0 and 255.

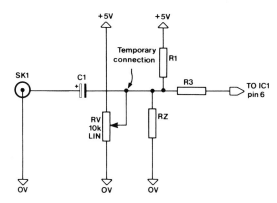

Fig. 9.8 Obtaining a variable voltage for testing the A-to-D converter.

If you do not obtain the results given above, check these points:

If the reading is always 255: faults in address decoding circuit, or you are using the wrong address; faults in the enabling circuit; IC1 is not converting, probably because the timing circuit is not providing the proper signals. You will need an oscilloscope to track down the source of trouble quickly; if a CRO is not available, check and recheck the connections. This is a complicated circuit but it is not 'tricky', and will work if it has been correctly wired.

Readings show 'binary errors' (i.e. errors which are caused by having a '1' where there ought to be a '0', or the converse). For example, if you get 144, 16 and 255 instead of 128, 0 and 255, data line D5 is 'stuck' at '1'. Check the wiring of this line from IC1 to IC2, from IC2 to IC3 and IC4, and from IC3 and IC4 to the data bus. Check the lines to the enabling inputs of IC3 or IC4. Also check the edge connector or other connections between the device and the micro. A table of decimal numbers and their binary equivalents will help you sort out which line is faulty.

Now type in a program to PEEK the address several times (say 100 times) and store the results. Use various potentiometer settings as described above. On each test the values should vary by no more than 1 or 2 from a given steady value. If there are any spurious values (e.g. the occasional 144 instead of 128), this is a binary error, as described above. There is probably an intermittent fault on one of the data lines. You can easily work out which line needs attention. Loosely wrapped connections or 'dry' solder joints are a frequent cause of intermittent faults.

Output circuit (Fig. 9.7)

Note the distinction between *analogue* ground and *digital* ground. IC9 has terminals for both. The digital ground is the 0 V line of the computer system. Analogue ground is connected to this at some point, and to the 0 V line of the power supply to the amplifier, but all connections to analogue ground should be close together so that the large return currents from the amplifier can not upset the action of the logic circuits. RV1 will normally be mounted on a panel, so connections to this go first to terminal pins on the board and then by multistranded wires to RV1. RV1 may also incorporate a switch to turn the independent power supply on or off.

The LM380 is a power amplifier capable of delivering 2 W to an 8 ohm speaker. When used at more than minimum power it becomes hot and needs a heat sink. If you are making a p.c.b. for this section of the circuit, provide an area of about 15 cm^2 of unetched copper, to which pins 3, 4, 5, 10, 11 and 12 are soldered. This area *must* be connected to audio ground. Alternatively, use a clip-on or stick-on heat sink, but remember that the pins listed above must be connected to audio ground.

The output from this circuit is of good audio quality so it is worth while employing a loudspeaker of reasonable size mounted in a proper loudspeaker enclosure. It may be possible to find room inside the enclosure for the main circuit board. With up to 29 lines coming from the computer it is advisable to use ribbon cable. This may be taken to a 'D' plug mounted on the wall of the enclosure (or case, if the main board is to be housed separately). If the board has an edge-connector area, another way of making the connection is to mount the board so that this projects through a slot cut in the wall of the case or enclosure. The ribbon cable is then terminated with an edge-connector socket which is pushed on to the projecting edge of the board. The only external controls to be panel mounted are the on/off switch for the amplifier power supply, and RV1, the volume control. It is possible to buy potentiometers which have a built-in mains switch.

Table 9.3 Components required

Resistors (carbon, 0.25W, 5% tolerance)

R1	1k2	R5	82k
R2, R3	3k9 (2 off)	R7	2k2
R4, R6, R8	390R (3 off)	R9	2R7
RV1	2M2 logarithmic volume control		

Capacitors

C1	10 μ' electrolytic
C2, C4	1 μ0, electrolytic
C3	2n2, polystyrene
C5	470 μ, electrolytic
C6	100n, polyester

Integrated circuits

IC1	ZN427 analogue-to-digital converter
IC2	74LS373 octal D-type latches
IC3, IC4	74LS125 quadruple bus buffer gates with three-state outputs
IC5	74LS13 dual 4-input Schmitt trigger NAND gates
IC6	CD4040BE 12-stage binary ripple counter
IC7	74LS30 8-input NAND gate
IC8	74LS00 quadruple 2-input NAND gate
IC9	ZN428 digital-to-analogue converter
IC10	LM380 audio power amplifier
IC11	74LS04 hex inverter buffer driver

Miscellaneous

Circuit board
SK1   coaxial or other socket for tape-recorder or microphone cable
LS1   loudspeaker 8Ω
IC socket 20 pin
IC socket 18 pin
IC sockets 16 pin (2 off)
IC sockets 14 pin (7 off)
Knob for volume control
Case/speaker enclosure
Edge connector or other multiway plug with ribbon cable for connections to micro (13 ways plus 8 or 16 address lines)
Components for making address decoder (see p. 7)
Components for making 12 V supply (see p. 19)

Programming

A BASIC interpreter runs far too slowly to allow sampling at audio frequency. If you prefer to use a high-level language, the obvious choice is FORTH. However, most of the programs you will need are very simple ones, so it does not take long to write them in machine code, even if you are a beginner.

The simplest program reads a single sample, and writes it straight back to the device without altering the value. The routine is:

> A: Load accumulator with contents of address PROC
> Store contents of accumulator at address PROC
> Jump to A

In the outline listing above, PROC is the address you have chosen for the Sound Processor device. The effect of this program is to reproduce the original sound apparently with no delay. This routine is useful for checking that the device is working properly, or for comparing normal sound with processed sound.

To produce an echo you need to take samples, store them in RAM and output them along with the current sample taken a fraction of a second later. You need a location in memory to act as a COUNTER. It may be more convenient to use one of the registers of the MPU as a counter. Two more bytes of memory are needed for STORE-1 and STORE-2. You also need to set aside a block of memory to hold the samples as they come in. About 10 K should be enough, though you can get a good echo with less. The first address in this block is referred to as the BASE address. The idea of the routine is to take an 'old' sample stored, say, half-a-second earlier and add a quarter of its value to three-quarters of the value of a 'new' sample. The sum of these values is then sent to the device. The routine is:

> A: Set COUNTER to zero
> B: Load accumulator with contents of address obtained by summing of the values in BASE and COUNTER (this gets the 'old' sample stored earlier)
> Divide accumulator by 4 and store it in STORE-1 (STORE-1 now holds OLD/4)
> Load accumulator with contents of address PROC (the 'new' sample)

Store accumulator in the address BASE + COUNTER (so putting NEW in place of OLD)

Divide accumulator by 4 (it is still holding NEW) store the result in STORE-2 (this gives NEW/4)

Load accumulator with contents of address BASE + COUNTER (this gets NEW back into accumulator)

Subtract from accumulator the value in STORE-2 (accumulator now holds three-quarter of NEW)

Add the value from STORE-1 (¼ OLD + ¾ NEW, which gives sound + echo)

Store accumulator at address PROC

Increment COUNTER

If the value in COUNTER now exceeds the total number of bytes to be stored, jump to A

Jump to B to process the next sample

A routine such as this repeats itself continuously. When the alloted block of memory is full it goes back to the beginning of the block and starts again. The bigger the block of memory, the longer the operation takes and the longer the delay between original sound and echo.

This routine gives a *single* echo. If after storing accumulator at address PROC, you also store it at address BASE + COUNTER, the sound plus echo is stored. This gives a series of echoes, dying away until they can be heard no more.

A very simple routine may be used to store a brief passage of sound in memory:

SET COUNTER to zero

A: Load accumulator with contents of address PROC

Store accumulator at BASE + COUNTER

Delay

Increment COUNTER

If the value in COUNTER is less than the total number of bytes to be stored, jump to A.

End

This gives a set of samples in memory, ready for processing or analysing. They can be 'played back' by using an almost identical program which has the addresses of the first two steps exchanged. The delay is optional. Without a delay it is probable that the MPU reads new samples faster than they are produced by the device. If you examine memory, four or five consecutive locations hold the same value, for the program is running four or five times faster than the device. The delay slows down the program, allowing storage of a longer passage of sound, or to reduce the amount of memory required for storage.

There are several interesting things to be done with the stored sound. You can chop off the ends of the passage to isolate a single musical note. Several of these are stored in memory and a program is written to play a particular note when a given key is pressed. The micro can be turned into an 'organ' which sounds like a piano, for example. You can deal with speech in a similar way, cutting it into the units of speech, or *phonemes*. Many of the speech-generating i.c.s. rely on a library of phonemes stored digitally. You can then program the micro to play back phonemes in a given order so as to synthesise whole sounds and sentences. It is probable that you will not have enough memory to store all the phonemes of English speech, but it should be possible to store enough for a limited vocabulary. Another approach is to store a selection of words and to program the micro to string these together to speak sentences. Dealing with sound in this way is a fascinating occupation. It will give you plenty of chance to make good use of programming skill.

Another way of treating stored sound is to subject it to frequency analysis. The usual method is a Fourier analysis, or transform which produces a 'frequency spectrum' showing which frequencies are present and their power. There is no space to describe the technique here, but it is dealt with in mathematical texts. Articles on the topic occasionally appear in computing periodicals (see reference on p. 135). If you are not in a hurry for the result, analytical programs may be written in BASIC.

Digital filtering is relatively simple and requires very little memory. A routine for a low-pass filter requires a single byte for STORE (or a register in the MPU could be used):

> Load accumulator with contents of address PROC
> Store content of accumulator at STORE (this starts the program with a 'previous' sample in STORE)
> A: Load accumulator with content of address PROC (this is the 'new' sample)
> Divide accumulator by 2
> Store contents of accumulator in STORE-2 (NEW/2)
> Load accumulator with contents of STORE-1

Divide accumulator by 2 (PREVIOUS/2)

Add contents of STORE-2 to accumulator (NEW/2 + PREVIOUS/2)

Store accumulator in address PROC (output mean value)

Store contents of accumulator in STORE-1 (ready to become previous sample next time round)

Jump to A

The way this works is explained on p. 118. You can vary the characteristics of the filter by altering way the samples are divided before summing. For example, you can take an eighth of the previous sample and add it to seven-eighths of the new one. This would make the output signal more dependent on the value of the current sample and less dependent on the previous sample. In other words the cut-off frequency of the filter would be higher. The pair of fractions must always total 1. For a fuller and very readable discussion of the theory of digital filtering and many other aspects of digital sound processing, see *Real Time Programming – Neglected Topics* by Caxton C. Foster (below).

References

Foster, C.C. (1981) *Real Time Programming – Neglected Topics*, Addison-Wesley Publishing Company: Reading, Massachusetts, USA.

Rogers, B. (1980) 'Fast fourier transforms'. *Practical Computing* (December), pp. 91-93.

Project 10
Digitiser pad

This project is similar to Project 4 in that it enables you to draw on a pad and have your drawing transferred to the screen. The difference is that its more complicated circuit allows it to operate much faster, transferring the picture on to the screen as rapidly as you can draw it. Its action is also more precise.

Table 10.1 The project in brief

Function: Drawings made on the pad are copied on to the screen of the micro. The pad is also used for entering data of many other kinds.
Interest: General, educational, games.
Power supplies: +5 V d.c., regulated, 160 mA.
Address bus: 1 address.
Data bus: 8 lines.
Control bus: Not required.
No. of i.c.s. 5.
Connection: either direct or through I/O port.

The circuit does much more of the data collecting in this project leaving the micro with far less to do. As a result it is easier to write programs to process the data before plotting it on the screen. For example, the scale of the drawing may be altered, allowing you to enlarge or reduce the displayed drawing almost instantly.

Another feature of the pad is that with suitable programming it becomes a user-defined key-pad. You provide overlays of your own design. Data and other information may be entered by touching the overlay with a probe. You provide overlays of your own design. Used in this way, the pad has many applications for games players.

How it works

Digitiser pads are available commercially, and usually cost about five times as much as the average personal computer. This is because they have very high resolution and many sophisticated features. This pad works in quite a different way to these, and gives a similar result though with lower resolution. Figure 10.1 shows how it works. The clock produces pulses at 50 kHz. These are fed to two 4-bit binary counters. The output of Counter 1 starts at 0000 (decimal 0), increases in binary fashion to 1111 (decimal 15) then returns to 0000 and begins again. Thus it runs repeatedly through all the 16 binary numbers from 0000 to 1111. As it changes back from 1111 to 0000, a single count is registered on Counter 2. This is also a 4-bit binary counter, running from 0000 to 1111, but at one-sixteenth of the rate of Counter 1.

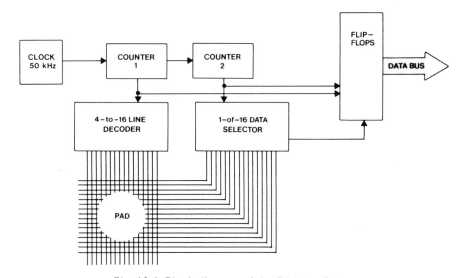

Fig. 10.1 Block diagram of the Digitizer Pad.

The outputs of Counter 1 go to a 4-to-16 line *decoder*. This has 16 outputs. Normally all these outputs are in the high state (+5 V), except for one, which is low (0 V). If the inputs from Counter 1 are 0000, then output 0 is low and all others are high. When the count becomes 0001, output 0 goes high and output 1 becomes low. The same happens for all other combinations of input from the counter. As the counter cycles, each output of the decoder goes low in turn. At 50 kHz, this cycle is repeated more than 3000 times a second.

Counter 2 has a 1-of-16 *data selector* connected to it. This receives four inputs from the counter and has 16 data inputs. It selects one of these data inputs at a time, depending on what combination of inputs it is receiving from the counter. If the inputs from the counter are 0000, it samples data input 0 to find out what datum is there. The datum which is at input 0 appears inverted at the single output. As counter 2 runs from 0000 to 1111, each of the 16 inputs are sampled in turn and the data on them appears at the output.

The pad acts to connect one of the outputs of the decoder with one of the data inputs of the selector. Figure 10.2 shows a section through a part of the pad. The outputs of the decoder are connected to 16 alternate copper strips on a piece of strip-board. The strips between these are covered by a thin strip of insulating tape. Resting on the tape (but not touching the bare strips) is a sheet of flexible plastic. This is painted with 16 stripes of conductive paint which run at right angles to the bare copper strips. They are about the same width as the strips and spaced the same distance apart (0.2 inches). One edge of the plastic film is folded around the edge of the circuit board, folded back to expose the painted stripes, and held in place by an edge connector. Alternate contacts of this press against the stripes. These contacts are wired to the inputs of the data selector. When pressure is applied to the plastic sheet (when a pencil or probe is pressed downward on it), one of the painted *stripes* comes into contact with one of the bare copper *strips*.

At each stage of Counter 2, Counter 1 runs through all its 16 stages. This means that while the selector is sampling one of its input lines (painted stripes), the decoder makes each one of its output lines (copper strips) low in turn. If one of these strips has been pressed into contact with the sampled stripe, a low level is passed to the selector. Its output then goes high.

It is convenient that an unconnected TTL input acts as if it has a high input. When a stripe is not in contact with a strip, it counts as a high input and the output of the selector stays low. The selector is made to sample each stripe in turn and, as each stripe is sampled, each of the strips are made low in turn. Since there are 16 strips and 16 stripes, there are 256 crossing points. Eventually the point is found at which contact is being made. A low level appears on the contacted strip and there is a high output from the selector.

The outputs from the counters also go to a set of eight D-type

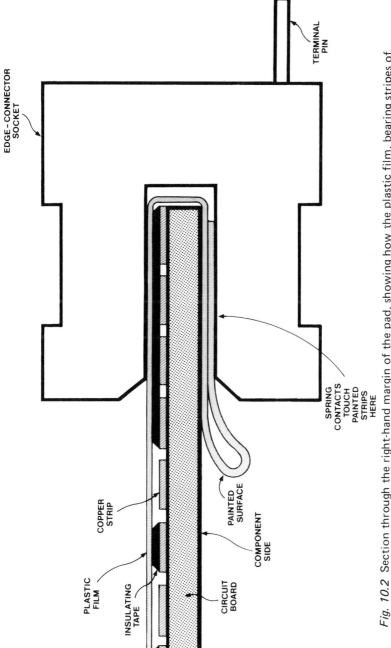

EDGE – CONNECTOR SOCKET

TERMINAL PIN

SPRING CONTACTS TOUCH PAINTED STRIPS HERE

COPPER STRIP

PAINTED SURFACE

COMPONENT SIDE

PLASTIC FILM

INSULATING TAPE

CIRCUIT BOARD

Fig. 10.2 Section through the right-hand margin of the pad, showing how the plastic film, bearing stripes of silver-loaded conductive paint is held in position.

flip-flops. In effect, the outputs make up an 8-bit binary number which repeatedly cycles from 0000 0000 to 1111 1111 (decimal 255). Each of these 256 values represents a point on the pad where a strip crosses a stripe. It is as if the crossing points were numbered from 0 to 255 running from the top left corner to the bottom right corner. When a strip and stripe are pressed into contact, the number of the strip (counter 1) and stripe (counter 2) are present at the inputs to the flip-flops. Together, these numbers make up the number of the crossing point. The resulting high-going pulse causes this number to be latched into the flip-flops. This cycle of 256 steps is repeated about 200 times a second. Each time round, the number of the crossing point where contact is being made is transferred to the flip-flops. To find out where the pencil is pressing, the micro only has to read the data from the flip-flops. It reads an 8-bit number, which is the number of the crossing point. It has no further calculations to perform, for it now knows exactly where the pencil is.

Construction

The original version of this circuit was built on a piece of strip-board measuring 22 by 9.5 cm. There were 38 strips, running lengthways along the board. The board was mounted strip-side uppermost, with the components on the underside, at the rear half of the board. The strips were left clear on the front half of the board to form the basis for the pad. Three strips on the left-hand edge of the pad area were covered with plastic insulating tape, and likewise four strips were covered on the right-hand edge (as in Fig. 10.2). The remaining 31 strips were alternately bare (16 strips) and covered (15 strips). About 1 cm was left clear at the far end (rear) of the board for the attachment of an edge-connector socket, connected to the computer by ribbon cable and a multi-way plug.

It is not possible to recommend any particular source of plastic film. A rectangle measuring about 9.5 x 14 cm is sufficient. It should be flexible and thin, but not so thin that it sags and touches the copper strips. It should bend easily when pressed, yet be sufficiently resilient to recover when pressure is removed. There should be no difficulty in obtaining a suitable sheet: for the proto-type, a piece was cut from a plastic wallet in which a program tape and handbook had been bought.

A fine watercolour brush is suitable for painting the stripes. Begin by drawing 16 parallel lines 0.2 inches apart on an area of paper the same size as the plastic film. The lines run lengthways along the rectangle. Assuming the film is transparent, lay the film on the paper. Paint stripes about 0.1 inches wide, being guided by the lines on the paper. Remember to stir the paint well before use and several times while you are painting.

The only thing which might go wrong is that the solvent of the paint softens the plastic. This is unlikely to happen, but it is worthwhile testing a small portion of the plastic with a few dots of paint before starting to paint the stripes.

It is important that the stripes should conduct well. Try to avoid thin regions in the stripes and, if necessary, overpaint regions which look too thin. It does not matter if the stripes are irregular in width, provided that adjacent stripes do not run together. When painting is finished, put the film in a warm place to dry for several hours. There is little point in testing for electrical continuity until the paint is fully dry, for conductivity is very low when the paint is wet. As it dries, the particles of silver come into contact and conductivity increases considerably. When the paint is dry, test each stripe by placing the probes of an ohmmeter at either end. If any show poor conduction or do not conduct at all, repaint these and leave the film to dry again.

Build the oscillator and counter circuits first (Fig. 10.3). IC2 contains both counters. The 'D' output of Counter 1 is used to trigger Counter 2 (pin 6 to pin 13). You need an oscilloscope to test for correct operation. There is a 50 kHz square wave at IC1 pin 6. It does not matter if it is as low as 30 kHz. Output A of counter A is at half this rate and B shows the rate halved again. This continues down the chain until the output at output D of Counter B is about 200 Hz. If you do not have an oscilloscope, you could connect a crystal earphone (through a 100 nF capacitor, with the other wire connected to the 0 V line) to outputs B, C and D of Counter 2 and hear notes at 800, 400 and 200 Hz respectively. This confirms that the counters are operating correctly.

Next, wire up the decoder (IC4). Note that its two strobe inputs (G1, G2) are to be connected to 0 V. When this is tested, each output line is normally high, but with an oscilloscope you will see a 1.25 μs low pulse every 20 μs. Wire the outputs to the copper strips and test each strip to detect the low pulses. If there is failure on any line, check the wiring to the strip and also the

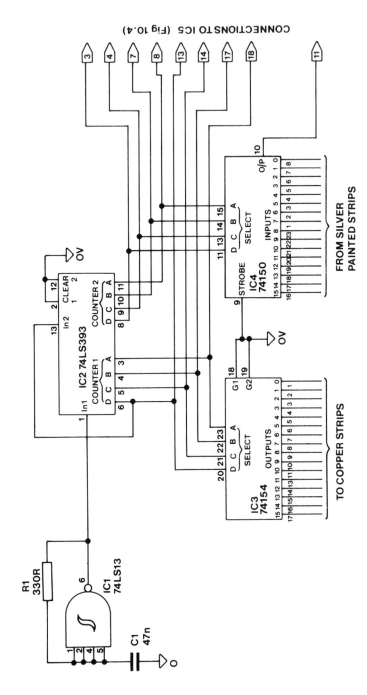

Fig. 10.3 Circuit diagram of the Digitizer Pad: the scanning circuits.

connections between IC2 and IC3. A dry joint between IC2 and IC3 could cause a number of strips to be inactivated. If *no* strips show the low pulse, check the strobe inputs to see that they are properly wired to the 0 V line.

Table 10.2 Connections not shown in Figs 10.3 and 10.4

	To 0 V	To +5 V
IC1	pin 7	pins 9, 10, 12-14
IC2	pin 7	pin 14
IC3	pin 12	pin 24
IC4	pin 12	pin 24
IC5	pin 10	pin 20

Table 10.3 Components required

Resistor

R1   330R, carbon, 0.25 W, 5% tolerance

Capacitor

C1   47n, polyester

Integrated circuits

IC1	74LS13 dual 4-input Schmitt trigger NAND gates
IC2	74LS393 dual 4-bit binary counters
IC3	74154 4-line to 16-line decoder/demultiplexer
IC4	74150 1-of-16 data selector/multiplexer
IC5	74374 octal D-type flip-flops

Miscellaneous

Circuit board approximately 22 x 9.5 cm
i.c. sockets, 24-pin d.i.l. (2 off)
i.c. socket, 20-pin d.i.l.
i.c. sockets, 14-pin d.i.l. (2 off)
Edge connector socket, 2.5 mm centres, single-sided, 32-way
Sheet of plastic film (see text)
Silver-loaded electrically conductive paint (2-3 grams)
Case or mounting board
Edge connector or other multiway plug with ribbon cable for connections to micro (10 ways plus 8 or 16 address lines)
Components for making address decoder (see p. 7)

At this stage apply the insulating tape to the copper strips. The easiest way to prepare the strips is first to cut a 9.5 cm length of insulating tape. Place this sticky-side downward on a clean sheet of glass or metal and press it gently into contact with the sheet. Use a steel edge as a ruler and cut the tape into narrower strips about 2 mm wide, using a sharp-pointed kraft knife or scalpel. Use forceps or tweezers to peel each strip from the sheet and place it sticky-side down on the alternate copper strips. These are the strips which are NOT wired to IC3. Cut two wider strips of tape for the edges of the pad area.

Next make the connections to IC4. The output may be tested by connecting a flying lead to the 0 V line and touching this against any one of the input pins (1-8, 16-23). The output is low except for a 20 μs high pulse every 320 μs. When no input pins are at 0 V, the output is continuously low.

Assuming it is dry and has been satisfactorily tested for electrical continuity, place the painted plastic film face downward on the pad area of the board. Bend it over the right-hand edge, as in Fig. 10.3, and fold it back to expose the painted stripes. Slide an edge-connector over it to grip it and hold it firmly in place, alternate contacts being aligned and pressing against the stripes. Use adhesive tape to fix the other three edges of the plastic sheet to the circuit board. Make the connections between the edge-connector and IC4.

Finally, connect the counters to the flip-flops (Fig. 10.4). These have three-state outputs so may be wired directly to the data bus.

The pad is now ready for testing. Plug it into the computer and run a simple program which repeatedly reads the output of the pad and displays it on the screen. In BASIC, a suitable program would be:

```
10  X = PEEK (60000)
20  PRINT X
30  FOR J = 1 TO 500: NEXT J
40  GOTO 10
```

Substitute your chosen address of the pad in line 10. With the delay provided in line 30, the pad is read about twice a second. While the program is running, move a pencil or blunt stylus around the pad. The numbers appearing on the screen range between 0 and 255. If the pencil is held still or if it is removed from the pad, the same number is repeatedly displayed. This is because the latches are refreshed only when the clock input of IC5 goes high. If there is no point of contact between a strip and a stripe, the output of IC4 remains low and the old data remains latched.

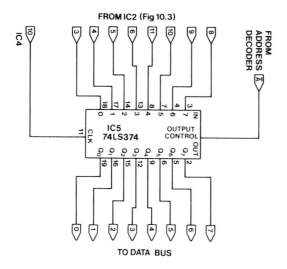

Fig. 10.4 Circuit diagram of the Digitizer Pad: the data output latch.

The plastic film may now be covered with a sheet of thin drawing paper, and the Digitizer Pad is ready for use.

Programming

The process of reading the Pad is extremely simple, as shown by the program above. Having obtained this data, there are many things which can be done with it, depending on the facilities of your micro. A simple calculation converts the data into a pair of coordinates for plotting a point on the screen.

The pad has only 16 x 16 resolution. Unless you are using very low-resolution graphics, or are displaying the picture on a small area of the screen, you will need to program the micro to join up consecutive points to make a continuous line. The joining routine should only come into play when the pencil moves from one point to an adjacent point. A simple subroutine can establish this fact. If the pencil has been found to move to a point which is *not* adjacent to its previous point, the pencil has obviously been lifted from the paper to begin a new line. The joining routine is not used in this event and a new line is begun.

An interesting application is to use the Pad in conjunction with the Sound Processor (Project 9). A waveform is drawn on the pad and is read by the micro. This data is used to generate a sequence of values as if a real sound had been sampled. The values are stored in the RAM. The sequence of values is sent repeatedly to the digital-to-analogue converter and so a new sound is created. Several different waveforms drawn separately on the Pad may be combined by the micro to generate even more complex and unusual sounds.

The Pad also has many uses for inputting data of other kinds. A simple example is a numeric keyboard, in which a piece of paper with the design of a keyboard drawn on it is fixed over the plastic film of the pad. The micro is programmed to read the pad and convert the number of any of the contact points within the area of a 'key' into the appropriate number on the keyboard design. This idea can be extended to all kinds of special-purpose keyboards. For example, it can be used as a menu selector in conjunction with any suitable program. The idea of menu selection and drawing can be combined by setting aside a narrow strip of along one edge of the Pad. The first 16 contact points could be designated as menu choice keys. If the pencil is used on other areas of the Pad a drawing is made in the usual manner, but if it touches a point in the menu-selection area, a choice of function is exercised. Functions which might be included in a scheme of this sort include: choice of background colour; choice of line colour; instructions to draw given shapes such as circles or squares when the pencil merely indicates the essential coordinates (such as the two diagonally opposite corners of the square or the centre and a point on the circumference of the circle); the instruction to fill in a given area with colour.

It is an interesting exercise in programming to devise a method of using the pad for a simple game, such as Noughts and Crosses. The players will need a supply of paper, each sheet having the 3 x 3 playing grid marked on it. The micro is programmed to find out which squares of the grid have been written in and whether the character is a 'O' or an 'X'. The latter operation may prove tricky, but the essential feature of the 'O' is that it has a hole in it, whereas the 'X' does not. The program should be able to check that each person plays in turn, and should assess the progress of the game at each move to discover the winner. Other games such as Battleships or maze games present an even greater challenge to the programmer, as well as to the players.

Project 11
Telephone modem

The purpose of this device is to allow you to send data from one micro to another over the public telephone network. Because it is not at present legal to connect a micro directly to the telephone line, except by means of commercially made devices which have been officially approved, the Modem is coupled to the line acoustically. The signal from the Modem goes to a loudspeaker which is placed near the telephone mouthpiece. Signals arriving at the telephone earpiece are picked up by a microphone and then processed by the Modem.

Table 11.1 The project in brief

Function: Transmission of data from one micro to another by telephone.
Interest: General.
Power supplies: +5 V d.c. regulated, 140 mA (including power to operate
  −5 V converter i.c.).
Address bus: 2 addresses.
Data bus: 1 bit
Control bus: $\overline{\text{RD}}$ and $\overline{\text{WR}}$, or R/$\overline{\text{W}}$
Connection: Direct or through I/O device.
No. of i.c.s: 7.
Special points: The modem i.c. is CMOS so requires special handling (see p. 22), especially as it is expensive. Two modems are required for transmission and reception data. An oscilloscope is almost essential for setting up the circuit.

It should be pointed out that in order to make use of this project, you need a friend or colleague who also has a modem of a similar type. It also helps if you both have the same type of micro, though this is not essential.

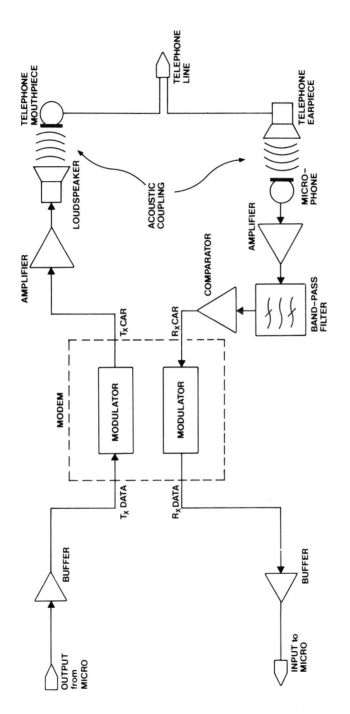

Fig. 11.1 Block diagram of the Telephone Modem.

How it works

This project is based on a single i.c. which contains the essential modem circuitry. As Fig. 11.1 shows, the modem i.c. is in two sections. One section, the *modulator*, produces an audio-frequency sine wave which it modulates according to the data coming from the micro. The sine wave is digitally generated and alternates between two frequencies. One of these represents '0' and the other represents '1'. Table 11.2 lists the frequencies; note that it is conventional that Channel 1 frequencies are used by the station which originates the transmission, while Channel 2 frequencies are used by the station which is answering. This means that it is possible to have simultaneous two-way communication between micros, though to program this without using additional hardware is a somewhat difficult task. It is simpler to keep to one-way communication and arrange that the micros transmit to each other alternately.

Table 11.2 Standard frequencies (Hz)

Function	Bit value	CCITT standard	US standard
Channel 1 (originating transmission)	0	1180	1070
	1	980	1270
Channel 2 (answering transmission)	0	1850	2025
	1	1650	2225

The remainder of the circuit on the transmitter side consists of a buffer and an amplifier. The buffer receives data (a series of '0's and '1's) from the micro and passes it on to the modulator through the Tx DATA input. The frequency-modulated sine wave signal comes from the Tx CAR (= carrier) output, is amplified and sent to the loudspeaker. This audio signal is detected by the telephone and sent along the telephone line to the other modem.

When a modem has originated a signal (on Channel 1), its demodulator section is tuned to receive the reply on Channel 2. The signal arrives over the telephone wire, is picked up by the microphone and is then amplified. At this stage it will have a considerable amount of background noise and distortion. A band-pass filter supresses signals of frequency outside the range of the modem. A comparator converts the resulting signal into a true square-wave signal of the two receiving frequencies. This is fed to the Rx CAR input of the modem. This signal is then *demodulated*. It is from this dual function of MODulator and DEModulator that the MODEM derives its name.

The Rx data output delivers a high, or low, output depending on which of the two frequencies is being received at that instant. A buffer conveys this signal to the micro.

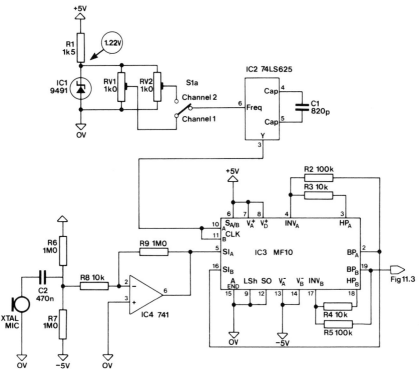

Fig. 11.2 Circuit diagram of the Telephone Modem: receiving circuit, with digital filter.

Figure 11.2 shows the receiving circuit in greater detail. The amplifier is a 741 operational amplifier wired as an inverting amplifier. Its signal goes to a digital filter i.c. (IC3). There is not space here to describe the details of the working of this i.c. It is connected as a 4-pole band-pass filter. Its centre frequency is determined by the rate at which its digital circuit is clocked. The clocking frequency is generated by a voltage-controlled oscillator (IC2). This oscillates at 100 times the centre-frequency to which the band-pass filter is to be tuned. The frequency of the VCO is

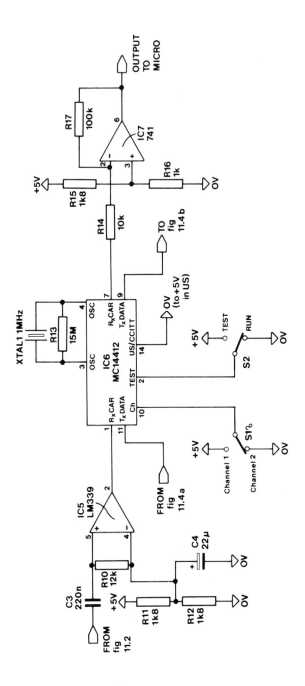

Fig. 11.3 Circuit diagram of the Telephone Modem: inputs and outputs of the modem i.c.

determined by the voltage supplied to it from the band gap voltage reference i.c. IC1. This provides a stable reference voltage of 1.22 V. Potential dividers (RV1 and RV2) tap this voltage at two levels so as to set the centre frequencies for Channel 1 (108 kHz) and Channel 2 (175 kHz). These voltages are selected by S1.

The filtered signal is passed to the comparator (IC5, Fig. 11.3). This is similar in many ways to an operational amplifier but has a much higher slew rate. The signal coming from this is a true square wave, and goes to the modem i.c. (IC6). The incoming signal is there demodulated and reappears at the Rx DATA output. It then goes to an operational amplifier (IC7) connected as an inverting amplifier with 10x gain. The main function of this is to serve as a buffer between IC6 and the micro. The signal from IC7 swings fully between 0 V and +5 V, so is suitable for feeding to an I/O device or to a one-bit input (see p. 7). If desired, it can be passed to the data bus, using a 74LS125 three-state buffer controlled by an address decoder, as shown in Fig. 4.3.

Figure 11.3 illustrates several features of the modem i.c. It requires a crystal oscillator to generate the transmission frequencies accurately. This is provided by the 1 MHz crystal, XTAL1, and resistor R9. The i.c. has several switchable functions. S1 is set according to whether the modem is on Channel 1 (originating a transmission) or on Channel 2 (answering). S1 is a double-pole switch which has been shown in Fig. 11.2 also, where it selects the appropriate centre frequency for the band-pass filter. S2 allows the modem to be tested. In the 'test' position, data which is being sent by the micro is sent back to the micro where it can be read and displayed. This test facility does not ensure that the audio coupling and telephone transmission are working properly, but is useful when developing programs.

Pin 14 of IC6 allows the two different sets of frequencies to be selected. In Europe it is more common to use the CCITT standard (International Consultative Committee for Telephone and Telegraph), whereas in the United States a different set of frequencies is favoured. In this design, pin 14 is grounded to provide the CCITT standard. For use in US it should be wired to +5 V instead. If you prefer, you can add a switch to select one standard or the other.

Figure 11.4 shows the circuits involved in transmission. A single transistor amplifier is used as a buffer between the micro and the modem i.c. The input to this may come from an I/O port or from a single data latch (as in Fig. 12.2). Certain computers have single-bit annunciator output ports (see p. 7) and one of these would be ideal.

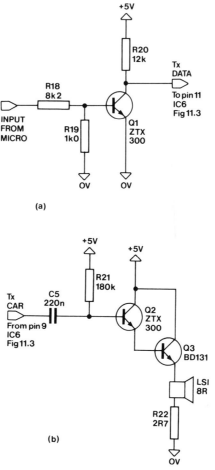

(a)

(b)

Fig. 11.4 Circuit diagram of the Telephone Modem: transmitting circuits;
(a) input buffer; (b) output amplifier.

From the modem, the modulated signal passes to a high-gain transistor amplifier (Q2, Q3, Fig. 11.4b) which drives the loudspeaker.

Construction

The circuit may be assembled on a piece of strip-board measuring about 11 by 9.5 cm. This size requires the components to be fairly densely packed. This is preferable for a circuit in which there are many high-frequency signals, for long leads and long connecting strips are liable to interfere between sections of the circuit. Since component density is to be high, some care is needed in planning the layout of the board. If you prefer to err on the safe side, begin with a board of slightly larger size than that mentioned above and cut away the surplus when you have finished construction. Alternatively, the spare space may be used to accommodate a UART (see Programming section).

Begin by building the circuit of Fig. 11.2. The −5 V supply for this may be taken from the micro, if available, since only a few milliamps are required. A single voltage converter circuit (Fig. 0.7c) may be used instead. Although its output may not be the full −5 V, this does not affect the operation of the circuit since only a nominal −5 V is required.

Note that if you wish to be able to switch between US and CCITT standards as described earlier, you will need to provide two pairs of preset potentiometers instead of the single pair shown in Fig. 11.2. You will also need to arrange that one pair or the other can be switched into use according to which standard is being selected at pin 14 of IC6.

Sheathed cable should be used for wiring the microphone to the circuit board, the sheath being connected to the 0 V line.

To test the circuit, switch on the power supplies. Check the voltage between R1 and IC1. This is typically 1.22 V, though it may lie between 1.20 and 1.25 V. Whatever voltage it produces is held with great precision despite changes of supply voltage and of temperature. Connect an oscilloscope to the output of IC2. Monitor the frequency and adjust RV1 and RV1 until the frequencies are 108 kHz and 175 kHz respectively. The testing of IC3 is left until later.

Next build the circuit of Fig. 11.3. A 10 MΩ and 3.3 MΩ resistor wired in series may be used instead of the 15 MΩ resistor (R9). Note that the comparator (IC5) and modem (IC6) derive their power supplies from the +5 V *and 0* V lines, but the operational amplifier (IC7) is supplied by the +5 V *and −5 V* lines. Table 11.3 gives details of connections not shown on the figures.

Finally, build the circuits of Fig. 11.4. The output amplifier of Fig. 11.4(b) requires a considerable amount of current so it is important to decouple this section of the circuit from the rest. It should be connected at the ends of the +5 V and 0 V rails most distant from the power source. A 10 μF electrolytic capacitor (C6) should be connected between the +5 V and 0 V lines. Its leads should be soldered to the lines at points *between* the output amplifier and the remainder of the circuit. This capacitor acts as a reservoir to prevent fluctuations in voltage level at the amplifier feeding back to the main circuit. Q3 may need a small heat sink if the device is to be operated for long periods in a confined space, but this is not normally necessary.

Table 11.3 Connections not shown in Figs 11.2 to 11.4

	To 0 V	To +5 V	To −5 V
IC2	pins 1, 8	pins 7, 14	−
IC4	−	pin 7	pin 4
IC5	pin 12	pin 3	−
IC6	pins 2, 5, 8, 13, 15	pins 6, 12, 16	−
IC7	−	pin 7	pin 4
C6	'−' wire	'+' wire	−

When power is applied to the circuit, a continuous note is heard from the loudspeaker. Its frequency depends on the setting of S1 and the state of the input from Q1. By temporarily connecting the input to 0 V, or to +5 V, and by putting S1 into each of its settings, the frequencies can be checked. For testing the receiving side of the circuit, the sound from the loudspeaker may be recorded on tape, holding the microphone of the tape recorder a centimetre or so away from LS1. The recording is played back into the microphone of the modem. The signal should be detectable at the output of IC4 and (provided that S1 is switched to the correct channel) at the output of the filter (IC3, pin 19). At this stage you may find it necessary to adjust RV1 and RV2 to set the centre frequency accurately for each channel. Since each channel has two frequencies (representing '1' and '0') which differ by 200 Hz, the filter must be tuned to pass both with equal amplitude. After tuning the filter, monitor the output from IC5. This is a square wave of the same frequency as the incoming signal. Finally monitor the output from the modem (IC6) as the pitch is changed. With the lower of the two pitches, the output from pin 7 is low (0 V), with the higher pitch the output rises sharply to +5 V. The output from IC7 is the inverse of this, since IC7 is wired as an inverting amplifier.

There are several ways in which the moden may be coupled to the telephone. The design of this is left to the ingenuity and skill

Table 11.4 Components required

Resistors (carbon, 0.25 W, 5% tolerance)

R1	1k5	R13	15M (or 10M + 3M3)
R2, R5, R17	100k (3 off)	R18	8k2
R3, R4, R8, R14	10k (4 off)	R19	1k0
R6, R7, R9	1M0 (3 off)	R21	180k
R10, R20	12k	R22	2R7
	R11, R12, R15, R16	1k8 (4 off)	

Preset potentiometers

RV1, RV2   1k0, cermet

Capacitors

C1	820p, silver mica
C2	470n, polyester
C3, C5	220n, polyester (2 off)
C4	22μ, electrolytic
C6	100μ, electrolytic

Semiconductors

Q1, Q2	ZTX300, npn transistor
Q3	BD131, npn power transistor

Integrated circuits

IC1	9491 band gap precision voltage reference i.c.
IC2	74LS625 dual voltage controlled oscillators
IC3	MF10 universal monolithic dual switched capacitor filter
IC4	741 operational amplifier
IC5	LM339 quad comparator
IC6	MC14412 universal low speed modem
IC7	741 operational amplifier

Miscellaneous

Circuit board
i.c. socket d.i.l. 20-pin
i.c. socket d.i.l. 16-pins (2 off)
i.c. socket d.i.l. 14-pin
i.c. sockets d.i.l. 8-pin (2 off)

S1	DPDT switch
S2	SPDT switch
XTAL1	oscillator crystal 1 MHz
XTAL MIC	crystal microphone or microphone insert
LS1	miniature loudspeaker (approx 4 cm diam), 8 ohm

Materials for mounting and enclosing LS1 and XTAL MIC (see text)
Components for building −5 V supply, if required (see Fig. 0.7c)
Components for building buffer interface, if required (see text)
Components for building address decoder, if required
Edge connector or other multiway plug with ribbon cable for connections to
    micro (4 ways, plus address lines and 2 control lines if buffers used)

of the reader. The microphone and loudspeaker must be held in position so that they are close to, but do not actually touch, the telephone handset. It may be necessary to experiment to find the ideal distances.

It is usual for the transducers (the loudspeaker and microphone) to be mounted on a block so that the telephone receiver may be inverted on them. Such a block may be cut to shape from a large block of plastic foam or expanded polystyrene. It helps improve appearance and durability if the block is fitted into a box. If the box has a deep lid this can be closed down over the telephone receiver during transmission to help exclude sound from the surroundings. Most modems have two wide tubes of rubber or similar material fixed around each transducer. The tubes are about 4 cm long and of such a diameter and shape that they grip firmly around the telephone receiver (earpiece and mouthpiece) when it is pushed into them. This seals off the air between the telephone receiver and the transducers, making the coupling more efficient and further helping to exclude extraneous sound.

Programming

In essence all that has to be done is to program the micro to send a series of '1's and '0's to the modem, or to receive and store the '1's and '0's coming from the modem. However, if one micro is to be able to communicate with another, this procedure must be done in an orderly fashion. Initially, the data to be transferred consists of a number of bytes, each consisting of 8 bits. The bits are sent one at a time, so the program must break up a byte into its eight bits and send each separately. This is easy to do by using a machine-code routine, and can also be done in BASIC.

```
10  X = PEEK (5000)
20  FOR K = 1 TO 8
30  Y = 0: IF K > 127 THEN Y = 1
40  POKE 60000, Y
50  X = X * 2
60  IF X > 255 THEN X = X - 256
70  FOR L = 1 TO 100: NEXT L
80  NEXT K
```

Line 10 reads the byte to be sent in turn. If its value is greater than 127 it means that the most significant bit is '1', if it is 127 or less, the most significant bit is '0'. Line 30 assigns Y, the value of the most significant bit. This is then poked to the port connected to the modem. The value of X is then doubled which, in binary terms, shifts all the bits one place to the left. If the top bit was '1' the new value of X is more than 255, so this must be subtracted (line 60). After a pause (line 70) to provide a pulse of the required length, the loop repeats to find the value of the next bit. When the eighth bit has been sent, the next byte is fetched.

The group of bits should be preceded by a start bit (usually a '1'), then the 8 bits follow and the group ends with a 'parity' bit. While it is sending the byte, the micro should keep a count of how many '1's have been sent. If 'odd parity' is decided on, the 'parity bit' is used to make up the total number of '1's in the group to an odd number. Thus, if the byte contains four '1's, the parity bit is a '1' to make the total odd. If the byte has five '1's, the parity bit is '0'. This feature allows the receiving micro to check that the byte has been received without error.

The receiving micro is programmed to wait for the start bit. It samples the input repeatedly until a high level is detected. This tells it to expect a train of 10 pulses, arriving at a rate which has already been agreed upon. The timing of the receiving program is such that having detected the beginning of the first pulse, it waits for one and a half periods and samples the input again. This tells it whether the first bit of the byte is a '1' or a '0'. It then samples the input at intervals of one period to coincide with the middle of each successive bit. Since there are only 10 bits to read, it does not matter if the timing of the receiving micro is slightly different from that of the sending micro, since it is unlikely to get out of phase during such a short transmission. When the byte has been received, the receiving micro checks the number of '1's to see if it is odd (assuming odd parity has been agreed as the standard). If so, it discards the parity bit, and forms the other 8 bits into a byte, which is stored in memory. If parity is wrong, it reports this fact to the operator. It then waits for the arrival of the next start bit. The interval between bytes need not be exactly timed. Timing begins anew with the arrival of every start bit.

This is a low-speed modem, capable of handling up to 300 bits per second (300 baud). The timing of your program should be such that this rate is not exceeded. A machine code routine is essential for operating at this speed. However, there is no minimum rate for transmission, so a program in a higher level language such as BASIC can be used just as easily, though more slowly.

As shown in Table 11.2, the modem i.c. transmits '0' as the higher of the two frequencies in the CCITT standard (the reverse applies in the US standard). The buffer between the micro and the modem i.c. inverts the signal coming from the micro, so a '0' from the micro results in the *lower* of the two frequencies being transmitted. At the receiving end, this causes the modem i.c. to give a *high* output, but this is inverted by the buffer and the micro receives a low input. Thus a '0' leaving one micro arrives as a '0' at the other. The double inversion of the signal is the result of the way the modem i.c. is coupled to the micros in this project, and this may not be the same for other modem equipment. In practice, there seems to be little standardisation on whether '0's and '1's are transmitted as the lower or higher frequency, so it is necessary to establish how the receiving modem operates before attempting to send signals. If further inversion is required, this can easily be done by modifying the programs.

The programming required for a modem can become rather complicated, especially if two-way transmission is to be attempted. There is a special i.c. called a Universal Asynchronous Receiver Transmitter (UART) — an example is the IM 6402 IPL. It accepts data from the transmitting micro a byte at a time and converts it into serial form, automatically adding the start bit and parity bit. You can set it to send a stop bit as well, and to operate with odd or even parity. The output of the UART goes to the modem for transmission. At the receiving end, the modem demodulates the signal and send it to another UART. Its receiving section takes the serial data as it arrives, checks the parity and outputs the data to the micro a byte at a time. There is no room here to describe the details of this kind of i.c., but it is worth considering the addition of such an i.c. to your modem after you have gained experience in its operation.

Project 12
Alarm clock timer

This project provides the micro with its own alarm clock. The micro is able to set the alarm to interrupt it after a certain period of time has elapsed. The unit period is about 15 minutes and the alarm can run for any number of unit periods up to 15, so the longest period which can be programmed is three hours and three quarters.

The timer is self-contained and, once it has been set, does not require the attention of the micro until the alarm time is reached. As explained in the programming section, it can be used to help the micro carry out a daily program of household operations, such as waking up the family in the morning, and switching on the porch light at dusk. It is a useful adjunct to the Electric kettle Controller (Project 1) and the Mains remote control system (Project 7).

Table 12.1 The project in brief

Function: An elapsed period timer, which interrupts the micro.
Interest: Domestic, hobbies, games.
Power supplies: +5 V d.c., regulated, 15 mA.
Address bus: 1 address.
Data bus: 4 lines.
Control bus: $\overline{\text{RD}}$ and $\overline{\text{WR}}$ or R/$\overline{\text{W}}$.
Connection: direct, or possibly through an I/O device.
No. of i.c.s: 5.
Special points: IC2-IC5 are CMOS. You need to know something about machine-code and the workings of your micro to make best use of this device, but it can be used with BASIC too.

Although the timer is designed for use with a daily routine, it is easily modified to work with a much shorter unit timing period. If the period is shortened to 2 minutes for example, it runs for periods of multiples of 2 minutes up to a maximum of half an hour. This has applications in process timing. In the photographic dark room, the micro sounds the Bleeper (Project 3) to indicate when each stage of processing is complete. With an even shorter unit time (for example 15 seconds) it is used for timing moves in game.

How it works

The timing is carried out by a clock (Fig. 12.1) which runs at about 2 Hz. The pulses from the clock are fed to a binary counter/ divider, which has 14 stages (IC2 Fig. 12.2). We use the outputs of the last 4 stages which give the original rate of counting divided by 2048 (2^{11}, pin 15), 4096 (2^{12}, pin 1), 8192 (2^{13}, pin 2) and 16384 (2^{14}, pin 3) respectively. The output at pin 4 makes an LED flash on and off about once every 30 seconds, as an indication that the timer is operating. The output at pin 15 changes once every 15 minutes, providing the unit timing period.

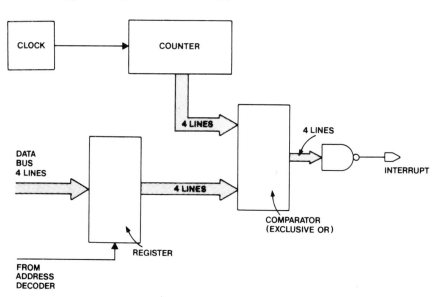

Fig. 12.1 Block diagram of the Alarm Clock Timer.

A period of timing begins when the counter is reset. This is done by an active-high READ pulse. As soon as the pulse goes low, the counter begins to register the pulses from the clock and the count is incremented every 15 minutes. The count is fed to a set

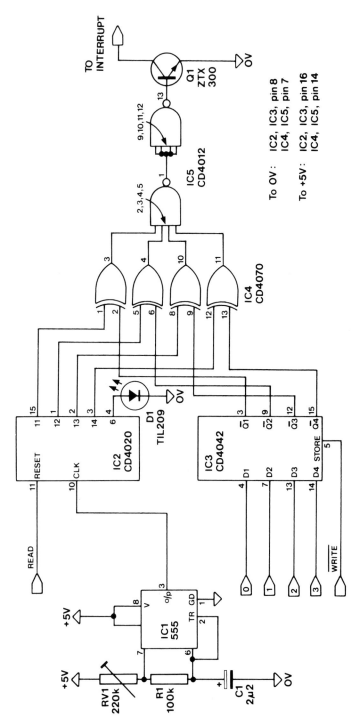

Fig. 12.2 Circuit diagram of the Alarm Clock Timer.

of four exclusive OR gates. The output of such a gate is high when both of its inputs are *equal*, but low when they *differ*. These gates compare the output of the counter with the output of the register (IC3). The register contains four latches, which are set by the micro at the beginning of the timing period. The number of unit periods required is put on to the data bus and an active-low WRITE pulse transfers this to the register. For example, if the micro is to set a period of 3 hours (12 unit periods) the number '12' (or rather '1100' in binary) is put on to the data bus and transferred to the latches. The outputs of the latches also go to the exclusive OR gates.

The count from IC2 increases gradually. When it reaches '1100' the two inputs of each gate become identical. At this point, and not before, the outputs of all four gates go high. The NAND gate has had a high output up to this point but, when all its inputs go high, its output goes low. The next NAND gate merely acts as an inverter. Its output changes from low to high. This turns on the transistor Q1 and a collector current flows through it. The collector is wired to an interrupt line of the micro. This line normally carries a high voltage (+5 V) but it can be pulled low by any one or more devices which may be attached to it. These often have a transistor output stage the same as shown here. When the level on the interrupt line goes low, the microprocessor finishes the operation which it is currently performing, puts all the relevant data concerning it on the stack (a special section of memory) and then jumps to an interrupt service routine (ISR).

The micro will have been programmed to take whatever action is appropriate at the end of the timed period. It might switch on a lamp, or sound the Bleeper. Having done this, it sets the timer to run for a further period, perhaps of different length, and then resumes the original program which it was executing at the instant it was interrupted. Operations such as switching on a lamp take the micro only a few milliseconds so that, if you happen to be playing a game on the micro at the same time it is interrupted, you would probably not notice that anything had happened.

Construction

Build the timer first — it operates at about 2 Hz (more exactly, 2.28 Hz to obtain a 15 minute unit period), so can easily be tested by connecting a voltmeter to pin 3. The needle oscillates rapidly showing that the timer is operating.

Wire up the counter and connect it to the timer. The output from the address decoder must be active-high. So that the timer needs only one address in memory, an active-high READ operation is used. The right-hand diagrams of Fig. 0.5 show how to obtain this. If you have not built the decoder yet, temporarily wire the reset pin to the 0 V rail to allow the counter to run for testing. When a voltmeter is connected to pin 9, the needle oscillates at about 4 Hz, for this is the output of the first stage of the counter chain. The LED flashes on and off once every 30 seconds. This LED can be used to adjust the unit period. For a 15 minute unit period, the LED comes on every 28.125 s (or 3 min 45 s to come on eight times). Adjust RV1 until the LED flashes at the correct rate.

Table 12.2 Components required

Resistors

R1	100k, carbon, 0.25 W, 5% tolerance
RV1	220k miniature horizontal preset

Capacitor

C1	$2\mu2$, electrolytic

Semiconductors

D1	TIL209, or similar light emitting diode
Q1	ZTX300, or similar npn transistor

Integrated circuits

IC1	555 timer
IC2	CD4020BE 14-stage binary counter
IC3	CD4042BE quad latch
IC4	CD4070BE quad exclusive-OR gates
IC5	CD4012BE dual 4-input NAND gates

Miscellaneous

Circuit board
16-pin i.c. sockets (2 off)
14-pin i.c. sockets (2 off)
Edge connectors or other multiway plugs with ribbon cable for connections
    to the micro (8 ways plus 8 or 16 address lines)
Components for making the address decoder

The latch i.c. is enabled by an active-low $\overline{\text{WRITE}}$ output from the address decoder. The left-hand diagrams of Fig. 0.5 show how to obtain this. Complete the wiring of the latches and exclusive or gates, then attach the circuit to the micro. If you POKE a 4-bit number (0 to 15 decimal, 0000 to 1111 binary) to the chosen address, this number appears at the outputs of the latch i.c. Use a voltmeter to test the outputs and also to monitor the state of the counter. Test the outputs of the exclusive OR gates from time to time. One or more of these is low, except when the counter shows the same number as the latch. Then all outputs are high.

Complete the circuit by assembling the NAND gates and transistor. The collector terminal Q1 goes to one of the interrupt lines of the micro. Many micros have a choice of two interrupt lines. A low level on the non-maskable interrupt ($\overline{\text{NMI}}$) line unfailingly interrupts the micro whatever it is doing. You could use this line when testing the device. Program the micro to set a time on the register, then run some other program. When the correct time is reached, the $\overline{\text{NMI}}$ line is made low and the micro stops running the program. This is not the way the alarm timer is normally used but is an easy way of testing that it works.

Programming

As explained above, the counter must first be reset. This is done by addressing the timer with a reading operation. In BASIC the command might be 'PEEK (60000)', where 60000 is the address of the timer. This sends a high pulse to the reset input of the counter and all its outputs go low. Follow this immediately with a command to POKE the required number of unit times to the same address. For example, the command 'POKE 60000, 4' sets the timer to run for one hour. Q1, Q2 and Q4 go low and Q3 goes high. The timer then operates independently. It interrupts the micro after one hour.

What happens at interrupt time depends on how the micro has been programmed. Different microprocessors behave in different ways so it is not possible to give details which apply to all. Normally you will not use the $\overline{\text{NMI}}$ line but an interrupt request line ($\overline{\text{IRQ}}$ or $\overline{\text{INT}}$). Whether the micro responds at all depends on whether it is allowed to do so. Many microprocessors can be set to ignore IRQs, or to pay attention to them only under certain circumstances.

The 6502 is fairly easy to program for interrupts, provided that you are able to write simple machine-code routines. Following an IRQ, the MPU goes to addresses FFFE and FFFF, to find the address of the interrupt service routine. It then jumps to the address which is stored there (low byte in FFFE, high byte in FFFF) and executes the program which begins at that address. The Z80 is less easy to use with this project, since Modes 0 and 2 of response to an interrupt require the interrupting device to provide the MPU with an address to jump to by placing it on the data bus. This project does not have that facility, though. In Mode 1 the Z80 jumps to address 0038, where there is usually a jump instruction which takes it to the interrupt service routine. In many Z80-based micros, this routine is in ROM and it may not be easy to get the MPU to go from there to RAM where you can place your own routines. This depends on the nature of the monitor program and the helpfulness of the manual which accompanies the micro.

If you are unfamiliar with machine code, or your micro does not lend itself to your using its interrupt lines, it is still possible to use the alarm timer. Instead of taking its output to an interrupt line, take it to a 1-bit input or to a port of an I/O device. You then program the micro to read the input at least once every 15 minutes. If it reads '1', it returns to whatever it was doing, but if it reads '0' it knows that the time has come for it to perform its alloted task. Programs for this style of operation can easily be written in BASIC or another high-level language.

A daily routine may be programmed as a series of timing periods each ending in a particular operation. For example, we could begin with switching on the electric kettle at 7 a.m. The micro switches this on, then sets the timer for a single unit period. A quarter of an hour later (7.15 a.m.), the micro is interrupted and sounds the waking alarm. At the same time it resets the timer for a period of one hour at the end of which it sounds the bleeper to remind the family that its time to get ready for school. It resets the timer again, and at the end of that period will perform another of its tasks. It continues in this way throughout the day, resetting the timer to call it back when the next task has to be performed. It keeps an account in its memory of how far it has reached in its daily program, so that it knows what to do each time it is called.

Its last call of the day is at midnight, when it switches off the porch light. It sets the next alarm call for three and a half hours later. The household will be sleeping when the micro is called at 3.30 a.m. and all it does is reset the time for a second period of three and a half hours. This brings it round to 7 a.m., when it is interrupted, turns on the electric kettle and the day begins again.